General Editor

Edwin Anderson
Vice-President, Waterloo Mathematics Foundation

Authors

Lloyd D. Auckland
Director, Waterloo Mathematics Foundation

Peter W.D. Crippin
Problems Chair, Canadian Mathematics Competition

Ronald G. Dunkley
President, Waterloo Mathematics Foundation
Director, Centre for Education in Mathematics and Computing

Barry A. Ferguson
Director, Canadian Computing Competition

Ruth S. Malinowski
Executive Committee, Canadian Mathematics Competition

Gordon T. Nicholls
Managing Director, Centre for Education in Mathematics and Computing

Ronald G. Scoins
Associate Dean, Faculty of Mathematics
Director, Canadian Mathematics Competition

All members of the writing team are from the Faculty of Mathematics at the University of Waterloo.

Foreword

Problems and How to Solve Them, Volume 1, is the first in a new series from the Canadian Mathematics Competition team, the same group that compiled the popular series Problems, Problems, Problems. Recognizing that for many students and teachers it is not sufficient to simply present sets of problems, good though they may be, this new series will contain, in addition to many problems, a discussion of various approaches and techniques that can be employed in solving the problems. Numerous examples have been included along with bits of historical background. In addition, lists of relevant formulas have been added to the discussion wherever they are deemed appropriate.

While the discussion and problems are useful to both teachers and students as a means of enriching mathematics, or as a way to prepare for mathematics contests, we hope that the changes will make it easier for students to use the book on an independent basis, and that their confidence in attempting problems will increase.

The problems have been selected, in part, from previous Pascal, Cayley, and Fermat Mathematics contests. For these we acknowledge the contributions of many teachers from across Canada who have served on our Problems Committees. All of these problems have been changed from a multiple choice format to a form requiring full written solutions. A few problems originated in the grades 10 and 11 Invitational Challenge papers. There are, however, numerous entirely new problems, created especially for this book by the authors, all of whom have extensive experience in posing innovative questions for young minds.

The authors wish to thank Bonnie Findlay for the many, many hours she spent in typesetting the manuscript and preparing the diagrams. Her patience and perseverance has been extremely valuable to all of us.

We would also like to thank Patty Mah for designing the cover and for looking after technical details such as the ISBN, copyrights, and the printing of the book.

The Canadian Mathematics Competition and the authors gratefully acknowledge the encouragement and assistance of the Faculty of Mathematics at the University of Waterloo in the production of this book.

Edwin Anderson
July, 1997.

Contents

Chapter 1   Introduction to Problem Solving

This book is about solving mathematical problems. What, you ask, is a mathematical problem? Well, in simple terms, a mathematical problem is called that because it causes us problems when we try to solve it. There are other mathematical questions that we call exercises, and by and large we can divide the questions that we face into two categories, exercises and problems.

An exercise is a question in which it is pretty obvious what one is expected to do. If, for example, you are given the equation $4x - 7 = 2x + 19$, with no instructions at all, you would almost certainly solve for x. Questions like this are exercises, and much of the homework you are expected to do consists of questions of a similar nature. These are important questions for you to work on because it is through them that you develop the skills that you will use in solving the more difficult questions called problems.

A question is a *problem* if it is not obvious what you should do. Consider the question

A license plate number consists of exactly 4 digits. How many different plates can be created in which the sum of the digits is 35 or greater?

It is *not* immediately obvious what you should do here. In fact, you have to think a little bit about what you might possibly do, because it isn't obvious that there is anything in your past experience that will help you get to a solution. However, after an initial bit of panic, stop and ask a few questions of yourself or, better still, of a friend. Your conversation might go something like this.

You.   "I'm trying to create numbers that have four digits that add up to 35 or more."

Me.   "How much more?"

You.   "It doesn't say."

Me.   "Maybe we can determine the largest possible sum."

You.   "Well, if it was all 9's that would be the biggest possible number, and that would give 9999."

Me.   "That's a great observation, because the sum of those digits is 36, so I guess the only possible sums of the digits are 35 and 36. How would you get 35?"

You.   "The only way would be to use three 9's and one 8."

Me.   "How many numbers can you create with three 9's and one 8?"

You.   "Let's see; we could have 8999, 9899, 9989, 9998, so there are four numbers."

Me.   "That's interesting. You could have said that there are four places to put the 8; the 1st, 2nd, 3rd, or 4th position, so there are four numbers *even if you don't list them*."

You.   "That's kind of neat. I've got the answer, then. There are five numbers in total, one using all 9's and four using three 9's and one 8."

Me.   "Golly, it wasn't so hard after all!"

This gives you a sense of the difference between an exercise and a problem. In the former, you proceed *almost* automatically. You don't want to become too complacent, because there are always pitfalls possible even in questions that look to be pretty routine. The big thing about problems is that they will rarely present routine challenges. You will almost always have to do some creative thinking before you can solve them. This sounds as though they are hard to crack, and that is frequently true. However, because they require some analysis before they can be solved, they are far more valuable in helping you develop good thinking patterns. Achieving success in solving problems is also far more rewarding, because not everyone can do it, and you will certainly derive a greater sense of satisfaction when you obtain a solution.

1

This book contains a set of problems based on a variety of topics. We start by discussing a few problems and compiling a list of steps you can follow in solving problems. For each of the topic sets we list facts with which you should be familiar and discuss examples illustrating their use.

We emphasize that knowing the steps is only part of the process. You can't solve problems by memorizing facts and steps, nor by rote learning. You may become stuck. If so, persist! We learn more from struggling with a problem than from one that is solved quickly. Talk to your classmates or your teacher. We can learn a lot from chatting about a problem.

Are you ready? Here we go!

ANALYZING A PROBLEM

Consider the problem:

> *How many natural numbers less than 150 leave a remainder of 3 when divided by 7 and a remainder of 4 when divided by 5?*

Step 1.   *Read the problem and ensure that you know what is to be determined.*
              Here you are asked to determine all those numbers less than 150 that give specific remainders when divided by 7 and 5.

Step 2.   *Review your knowledge of the properties that might assist in solving the problem.*
              What do you know about division? Take a moment to write down what facts you can; then see if they compare with those below.

Division Facts
1. 3 divides exactly into 39 because $39 = 3 \times 13$.

     When we can find a number b such that $p = qb$, with p, q, and b all integers, we say that q divides p exactly.

     For $p = 48$ and $q = 6$, what is b? $\boxed{b = 8}$

2. 3 does not divide exactly into 41 because there is no integer b that makes $41 = 3 \times b$. We can, however, write $41 = 3 \times 13 + 2$.

     When q does not divide p evenly, there is always a b and an r such that $p = qb + r$.

     Further, we can make r less than q.

     For $p = 58$ and $q = 7$, what are b and r? $\boxed{b = 8, r = 2}$

Step 3.   *Apply the properties you know in attempting to solve the problem.*
              Not everyone will approach a given problem in the same way as you. This is no cause for concern. In fact, it is one of the interesting things about problem solving. We will follow the analysis of three different students in this problem to illustrate this point.

Student A
This student doesn't see an easy way to get at the problem, but does know the division facts above. His thinking leads him to say that numbers giving a remainder of 3 when divided by 7, if listed, will include some of those giving a remainder of 4 when divided by 5. He reasons, then, that he could simply write them down. His list is:

3, 10, 17, 24, 31, 38, 45, 52, 59, 66, 73, 80, 87, 94, 101, 108, 115, 122, 129, 136, 143.

Numbers from this list that give a remainder of 4 when divided by 5 are 24, 59, 94, 129. His answer is the numbers 24, 59, 94, and 129, which is correct. (He is very happy that the question didn't say smaller that 500!)

Student B
Student B uses the second division fact to agree that if a number is divisible by both 7 and 5 it must be divisible by 35. Do you agree with this conclusion? Now she reasons that numbers that are not evenly divisible by 35 all have the form $35b + r$. If the remainder on dividing by 7 is 3, then the number must be of the form $35b + 3$, $35b + 10$, $35b + 17$, $35b + 24$, or $35b + 31$. Of these, the first gives a remainder of 3 when divided by 5, the second a remainder of 0, the third a remainder of 2, the fourth a remainder of 4, and the fifth a remainder of 1. The only one of these giving a remainder 4 is $35b + 24$, and for $b = 0, 1, 2, 3$ we obtain 24, 59, 94, 129. Here is a better approach in the sense that we need not write a long list of numbers.

Student C
Student C uses the second division fact to say that if a number n is what we want, then $n = 7b + 3$ and $n - 5c + 4$, and these must be equal for some b and c.

Hence $7b + 3 = 5c + 4$
$$7b - 5c = 1$$

The smallest b that allows a solution for this equation is $b = 3$, whence $c = 4$. Hence, $n = 24$. However, the equation is also satisfied by $b = 8, c = 11$; by $b = 13, c = 18$; and so on. We see that n can also be $7 \times 8 + 3 = 59$ or $7 \times 13 + 3 = 94$, or $7 \times 18 + 3 = 129$.

WHAT DO WE LEARN?
The solutions of students B and C give you something that is lacking in that of student A. Student B discovered that $n = 35b + 24$ gives an acceptable answer $b = 0, 1, 2, 3, ...$ and so on, and could list any numbers of acceptable answers. Student C discovered that $n = 7 \times (3 + 5m) + 3$ for $m = 0, 1, 2, 3, ...$ and so on. These students observed the *pattern* to their solutions. *Pattern recognition is extremely useful in problem solving.*

Summary
In solving problems, a listing of the steps followed by these students will always be of assistance.
1.   Read the question carefully. Make sure that you are very clear about what you are asked to do.
2.   Review those facts that you think may help you.

3.   Doodle if it helps. Try some numbers. Student A in our dialogue did that and *got the correct answer*. It wasn't as pretty as what Student B and Student C did, but it worked.

4.   Draw a picture if at all possible. The next example illustrates this. If you do draw one, make it big enough to help you!

5.   Don't get excited if there is a sense of panic. It happens to everyone.

6.   Look for a pattern. It won't always appear, but when it does, it can be a big help.

7.   Guess. You'll be surprised how often it helps you, and you'd be amazed at how frequently good mathematics students do it.

8.   Once you get a solution, write it down carefully. This is an extremely important step, because this is where you'll earn your marks if the work is graded.

9.   Remember that problem solving is like most things in life. Very few of us are very good at it initially. We all get better with practice, and then more practice.

10.   Reflect on your work. Does the answer obtained make sense?

WHY DRAW DIAGRAMS?

Here's another problem:

A rectangular house which measures 20 m by 10 m has an outside electrical outlet at one corner of the house. An electric mower, connected by a cord to the outlet, can reach a maximum of 15 m. What is the largest area of lawn that can be cut?

Following the recommended steps, you make sure that you understand the problem. It requires finding an area, but can you visualize the shape of the region?

The second step is to review facts that might help in solving the problem. What facts do you recall about electric cords and lawnmowers? How can they help answer the question, anyway?

Now you see the reason for a diagram. Remember, make it big enough that you can see what's going on.

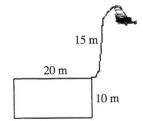

If the area is to be maximized, surely the cord should be fully stretched, and then swept to enclose the maximum area. Draw the diagram again.

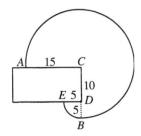

By stretching the cord to A and sweeping at a radius 15 m from C, part of a circle is traced, going to B. How much of a circle? You're right; it's three-quarters of a circle, and you can find that area, can't you? Now what's left over? Well, the chord has to lie along edge CD (that's 10 m). So starting at D there's 5 m left to swing from B to E, and that's one-quarter of a circle having radius 5.

Finally, you can do the problem. The area that you can cut is three-quarters of a circle with radius 15 plus one-quarter of a circle with radius 5, so the area is $\frac{3}{4}\left(\pi \times 15^2\right) + \frac{1}{4}\left(\pi \times 5^2\right)$

$$= \frac{675\pi}{4} + \frac{25\pi}{4}$$

$$= \frac{700}{4}\pi \quad \text{or} \quad 175\pi.$$

The area that can be cut is 175π m^2, or approximately 550 m^2.
Now you can see why drawing diagrams is a good idea!

Problems Don't Have to be Real
While it is true that many problems can be connected with the real world, the truth is that many good problems that stretch our thinking and help us develop our analytical skills are quite artificial. This in no way detracts from their value in helping us to become better mathematicians. Analyzing them usually helps us to develop our understanding of the structure of mathematics.

Example
Given that $(x - 3)$ is a factor of $x^3 + 5x + s$, determine the value of s.

Discussion
Following the suggested steps, it is clear that we want to find a value for s. The fact that will allow us to solve the problem is an understanding of the word factor. Before reading further, see if you can enunciate clearly in your mind what it means to say that $(x - 3)$ is a factor of $\left(x^3 + 5x + s\right)$.

Remember that $(x - 3)$ and $x^3 + 5x + s$ are just numbers.
If you said that one number is a factor of a second number if it divides evenly into that number, you are on the way to a solution. If you said that p is a factor of q if (and only if) there is a number r such that $q = pr$, then you are in a better position, because you now have two ways to get at the problem.
If you are completely comfortable with the thought that any algebraic expression can be considered to be a number for arithmetic purposes, then a solution will come quickly, as follows. If $x - 3$ is a factor of $x^3 + 5x + s$, then there must be a second factor, and it must be of the form $x^2 + ax + b$. (Can you see why?)
Then $(x - 3)\left(x^2 + ax + b\right) = x^3 + 5x + s$.
Now $(x - 3)\left(x^2 + ax + b\right) = x^3 + (a - 3)x^2 + (b - 3a)x - 3b$.
But this must be exactly the same as $x^3 + 5x + s$.

Therefore we can write

$$a - 3 = 0 \quad \left(\text{because } x^3 + rx + s \text{ is really } x^3 + 0x^2 + 5x + s\right)$$

and $a = 3$.

Now $b - 3a = b - 9 = 5$

and so $b = 14$.

Then $\quad s = -3b = -42$.

Using the idea that $x - 3$ must divide evenly into $x^3 + 5x + s$, we obtain

$$
\begin{array}{r}
x^2 + 3x + 14 \\
x - 3 \overline{\smash{\big)}\ x^3 \qquad\quad + 5x + s} \\
\underline{x^3 - 3x^2 \qquad\qquad\quad} \\
3x^2 + 5x \\
\underline{3x^2 - 9x} \\
14x + 5 \\
\underline{14x - 42} \\
s + 42
\end{array}
$$

Since the division must be exact, the remainder is 0.

Hence $s + 42 = 0$ and $s = -42$, as before.

Both solutions are sound. The first solution, because it involves a term-by-term consideration, allows us to avoid the possibility of a messy expression for the remainder. The second solution is, however, perfectly correct.

We conclude this chapter with a very quick consideration of problems involving the word "prove". Inexperienced problem solvers sometimes think that illustrating by example is sufficient to satisfy the question "Prove that ...". This is not true. In problems based on algebraic statements, we prove (or justify) the truth of a statement by showing - from the algebra - that no other conclusion is possible.

In problems based on geometry, we develop a system of basic facts or properties and, using them, justify the truth of other statements. The underlying fact is that we must, one way or another, convince the reader of our solution that the statement is true *because no other conclusion is possible*. The weakness of illustrating by an example or two, using numbers, is that a doubter can always say "but have you tried it with all possible numbers?" We illustrate with an example.

Prove that there is one, and only one, right-angled triangle in which the sides are integers and such that one side is three greater than the smallest and three less than the greatest.

Discussion

We begin a solution by letting the sides be a, $a - 3$, $a + 3$, as in the diagram.

We can now form an algebraic equation:

$$a^2 + (a - 3)^2 = (a + 3)^2.$$

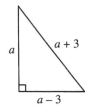

Hence $a^2 + a^2 - 6a + 9 = a^2 + 6a + 9$

$$a^2 - 12a = 0$$
$$a(a - 12) = 0.$$

Then $a = 0$ or $a = 12$.

If $a = 0$, $a - 3 = -3$ and we cannot have a triangle with a side of length -3. Therefore $a = 0$ is impossible.

If $a = 12$, $a - 3 = 9$ and $a + 3 = 15$ and we can have a triangle with sides 9, 12, and 15.

We have shown that there is a triangle meeting the conditions. Moreover, the algebra tells us that there is no other possible value of a, so we can safely conclude that there is only one such triangle. We have, then, *proven* that there is one, and only one, such triangle.

The following is a set of problems designed to test your ability to apply the principles discussed. There is no particular structure. Feel free to use any approach that you can think of.

Problems

1. A rectangular block has square ends and sides that are three units greater than one dimension of the end. If the total surface area is 210, what are the dimensions?

2. Determine how many pairs of positive integers (a, b) there are such that
$$a^2 + 3ab + 2b^2 - 10a - 20b = 0.$$

3. Prove that in a group of fourteen people there are at least two who have their birthday in the same month.

4. Determine all integer values of n such that both n and $n + 23$ are perfect squares.

5. At a meeting, each person present shook hands exactly once with every other person. If the total number of handshakes was 28, how many persons were present?

6. If $x^2 + 3x + 8$ is a factor of $x^4 + rx^2 + s$, determine r and s.

7. In the diagram, $ABCD$ is a square, P is equidistant from A, D, and E, and $PA = 10$. Determine the area of the square.

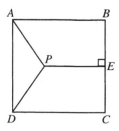

8. In the diagram $ABCD$ is a rectangle having $AB = 12$ and $AD = 9$. The lines AP and CQ are perpendicular to DB. Determine the length of PQ.

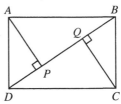
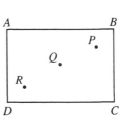

9. $ABCD$ is the boundary of a rectangular table. A ball shot at the edge will bounce off the edge, with angle of incidence equal to angle of reflection. There are three balls, at P (1 unit from AB and 2 from BC), at Q (in the middle of the table), and at R (2 units from AD and 1 from DC). If $AB = 8$ and $BC = 4$, at what point on DC should the ball at P strike if it is to miss the ball at Q and hit the one at R?

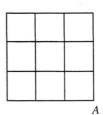

10. Each of $a_1, a_2, a_3, \cdots, a_{19}$ is a different integer chosen from the set $\{31, 32, 33, \cdots, 49\}$; that is, no two are the same. Prove that the product $(a_1 - 1)(a_2 - 2)(a_3 - 3)\cdots(a_{19} - 19)$ is always even.

11. The diagram shows the map of a nine-block housing region. Each block has houses along every edge. A security service wishes to set up a patrol system in which a guard will start at point A and walk along each street block at least once, but which requires the guard to walk a minimal distance. What is the minimum number of blocks that must be walked?

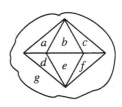

12. Is it possible to assign one each of the integers $1, 2, 3, \cdots, 7$ (with no repetitions) to the seven regions in the graph in such a way that numbers in adjacent regions (having a common edge) differ by (a) at least 2, (b) more than 2? If it is possible, how many different values are possible for region g? If it is not possible, write an argument to support your claim?

Chapter 2   *Arithmetic, Averages, Exponents*

In this chapter on the use of arithmetic, we hope to show some of its applications and how to unravel problems involving computation, percentages, powers, roots, averages, general number sense, and pattern. The joy of problem solving can be enhanced with understanding arithmetic and its uses.

What is the value of $6 - 2(5 - 1)$? On a recent contest almost 50% of grade nine students did not get the correct answer to a similar problem. Do you get the correct answer? The answer is -2, not 16. Why?

A person doesn't expect much difficulty in doing a simple arithmetic question. After all, the use of a calculator, or better still, the use of your own knowledge of addition, subtraction, multiplication, and division, should produce correct answers.

Besides these basic skills, order of operation is important. If you entered the question above into a calculator the answer would depend on the order of your presentation. These machines are no better than their operators. Thus, $6 - 2(5 - 1)$ becomes $6 - 2$ which is 4, and this result is multiplied by $5 - 1$, to give a result of 16. However, if the $5 - 1$ is entered first and then multiplied by 2 we get 8 and when this is subtracted from 6 we get -2. Obviously both cannot be correct.

Because of this, the order of operation rules have been standardized and we must first do work in brackets, then perform multiplication and division, followed by addition and subtraction.

What is the value of $2 + 3 \times 8 \div 6 - 24 \div 8$. In order to clarify the order, we insert some brackets. The question becomes $2 + (3 \times 8 \div 6) - (24 \div 8)$

$$= 2 + 4 - 3$$
$$= 3.$$

Notice that when there is only addition and subtraction, the order of operations is immaterial since

$$2 + 9 - 8 = 3$$
$$9 - 8 + 2 = 3$$
$$2 - 8 + 9 = -6 + 9 = 3$$

and $-8 + 2 + 9 = -6 + 9 = 3$.

Example 1
What is the sum of $1 - 2 + 3 - 4 + 5 - 6 + 7 - 8 + ... + 97 - 98 + 99 - 100$?

Solution
We could add all the positive numbers and then the negative numbers and then combine the results.
We could find $1 - 2 = -1$, $-1 + 3 = 2$, $2 - 4 = -2$, $-2 + 5 = 3$ etc., and notice a pattern.
The easiest way is to see that $1 - 2 = -1$, $3 - 4 = -1$, $5 - 6 = -1$, and so on.
There are 50 groups each with a value of -1, so the result is -50.

Sometimes arithmetic is complicated by numbers written in various forms such as 6% of 50, $\frac{2}{3}$ of 45, 2^5, $\sqrt{16}$, $\sqrt[3]{27}$, and $\sqrt{9+4}$. These should cause no difficulty if you understand the meaning of the symbols. The results are 3, 30, 32, 4, 3, and $\sqrt{13}$.

Decimals should be easy to add if you remember that we add and subtract only like units, that is, hundreds are combined with hundreds, units with units, tenths with tenths, etc. As for fractions, $\frac{1}{2} + \frac{1}{3}$ cannot be added until we write with like denominators:

$$\frac{1}{2} + \frac{1}{3} = \frac{3}{6} + \frac{2}{6} = \frac{5}{6}.$$

Exponents
Remember that a^{10} means $a \cdot a \cdot a \cdot a \ldots$ to 10 factors.

Combine this idea with what we have discussed earlier. For example, $2 - 5^3 = 2 - 5 \cdot 5 \cdot 5$
$$= 2 - 125$$
$$= -123,$$

whereas $(2-5)^3 = (-3)^3$
$$= (-3)(-3)(-3)$$
$$= -27.$$

Similarly $2 \div 5^3 = \frac{2}{125}$, whereas $(2 \div 5)^3 = \frac{2}{5} \cdot \frac{2}{5} \cdot \frac{2}{5} = \frac{8}{125}$.

The value of $3^4 \times 3^5 = 3^9$ (4 factors of 3 multiplied by 5 factors of 3). However, if we had to multiply $3^4 \times 5^3$, we could not add exponents because the bases are different. We must evaluate each and then add. Division of powers with like bases leads us to other conclusions.
For example, $3^5 \div 3^5 = 3^{5-5}$
$$= 3^0$$
$$= 1$$

and $4^2 \div 4^{-5} = \frac{4^2}{4^{-5}}$

$$= 4^7.$$

If $5^0 = 1$ and $5^{-2} = \frac{1}{5^2}$, what does $5^{\frac{1}{2}}$ mean?

Since $5^{\frac{1}{2}} \times 5^{\frac{1}{2}} = 5^{\frac{1}{2}+\frac{1}{2}} = 5$, the question is, "what are two identical factors that when multiplied together give 5?" The answer is $\sqrt{5}$.

Similarly $10^{\frac{1}{2}} = \sqrt{10}$, $10^{\frac{1}{3}} = \sqrt[3]{10}$, and, in general $10^{\frac{1}{n}} = \sqrt[n]{10}$.

What does $10^{\frac{2}{3}}$ mean?

$$10^{\frac{2}{3}} = \left(10^{\frac{1}{3}}\right)^2$$

$$= \left(\sqrt[3]{10}\right)^2$$

or $\quad 10^{\frac{2}{3}} = \left(10^2\right)^{\frac{1}{3}}$

$$= \sqrt[3]{10^2}.$$

What does $4^{-\frac{1}{2}}$ mean?

$$4^{-\frac{1}{2}} = \frac{1}{4^{\frac{1}{2}}}$$

$$= \frac{1}{\sqrt{4}}$$

$$= \frac{1}{2}.$$

Here is a summary of the tools you need to operate with powers.

- $a^n = a \cdot a \cdot a. \ldots$ to n factors
- $a^{-n} = \dfrac{1}{a^n}$
- $a^0 = 1$
- $a^{\frac{1}{n}} = \sqrt[n]{a}$
- $a^{-\frac{1}{n}} = \dfrac{1}{\sqrt[n]{a}}$
- $a^b \cdot a^c = a^{b+c}$
- $a^b \div a^c = a^{b-c}$.
- 0^0 is not defined.

Example 2

If $10^{2y} = 25$, find the positive value of 10^{-y}.

Solution
First of all, notice the question did not ask you to find y. Can we proceed from 10^{2y} to 10^{-y}?

We could take the positive square root of both sides of the equation $10^{2y} = 25$

to give $\left(10^{2y}\right)^{\frac{1}{2}} = 25^{\frac{1}{2}}$

$$10^y = 5.$$

Therefore $10^{-y} = \dfrac{1}{10^y} = \dfrac{1}{5}.$

Alternatively, we could write $10^{-y} = \dfrac{1}{10^y}$

$$= \sqrt{\left(\frac{1}{10^y}\right)^2}$$

$$= \sqrt{\frac{1}{10^{2y}}}$$

$$= \sqrt{\frac{1}{25}} \qquad \text{(since } 10^{2y} = 25\text{)}$$

$$= \frac{1}{5}.$$

If a negative answer were allowed, could the result have been $-\dfrac{1}{5}$? Check to see why this is possible.

Example 3
Find the values of x and y such that $2^{x+1} + 3^y = 3^{y+2} - 2^x$.

Solution
This looks difficult since we can't evaluate any of the terms, and there is no easy way of combining different bases.

Let us rewrite the equation in the form $2^{x+1} + 2^x = 3^{y+2} - 3^y$. \qquad (1)

Is this any better? Perhaps we can combine $2^{x+1} + 2^x$. If we remember that $2^{x+1} = 2^1 \cdot 2^x$, then

$$2^{x+1} + 2^x = 2^x \cdot 2^1 + 2^x$$

$$= 2^x\left(2^1 + 1\right)$$

$$= 3\left(2^x\right).$$

Similarly, $3^{y+2} - 3^y = 3^2 \cdot 3^y - 3^y$

$$= 3^y\left(3^2 - 1\right)$$

$$= 8\left(3^y\right).$$

Now, equation (1) becomes

$$3\left(2^x\right) = 8\left(3^y\right)$$
$$3^1\left(2^x\right) = \left(2^3\right)\left(3^y\right)$$
$$\frac{2^x}{2^3} = \frac{3^y}{3^1}$$
$$2^{x-3} = 3^{y-1}.$$

Can a power of 2 ever equal a power of 3?

Yes, just once, because $2^0 = 3^0 = 1.$

Therefore $x - 3 = 0$ and $y - 1 = 0$.

Thus $x = 3$ and $y = 1$ is the solution.

Just a note here. Exponentials can be rewritten in different forms using logarithms. If you are interested, look in a text that explains logarithms and open another topic in mathematics.

Averages

We can find the average of any numbers of elements in a set by dividing the sum of all of the elements in the set by the number of elements. For example, the average of a set of numbers such as 5, 7, 72, –11, 0, and 17 is $\dfrac{5+7+72-11+0+17}{6} = \dfrac{90}{6} = 15.$

If each element in the set is replaced by the average, 15, the sum would remain constant at 90. If another 15 was added, you would think the average would remain the same, and so it does since

$$\frac{90+15}{6+1} = \frac{105}{7} = 15.$$

If the average of three numbers is 18, what is their sum? Their sum would be 54, since, if we assumed all the numbers were equal, the three 18's sum to 54. The three numbers could have been anything as long as the sum was 54. If one number was 18, and another number was 11, the third number would be $18+7 = 25$. Why?

If we want the average to remain 18 we could increase one number by any amount as long as we reduced the total of the others by that same amount.

Baseball batting averages are the total number of successful "at bats" divided by the total number of at bats, and then this quotient is written as a percentage. Remember that $75\% = \frac{75}{100} = \frac{3}{4} = 0.75.$ Baseball statistics usually are given to three figure accuracy.

Thus a player who has 35 hits in 140 at bats has an average of $\frac{35}{140} \times 100 = 0.250$. Newspapers often write the average as 250.

If the player is successful in his next at bat, his average will be $\frac{36}{141} = 0.255$ (rounded off). If he is unsuccessful in his next at bat, his average will be $\frac{36}{142} = 0.254$ (again rounded off).

We should be careful in talking about averages. If we talk about the average age of a group, it doesn't mean that half the people are older and half are younger (that is the median); it means that the sum of the ages is the same sum as if every person were the average age.

Example 4
In her latest game, Mary bowled 199 and this raised her average from 177 to 178. What must she bowl in her next game if she wishes to raise her average to 179?

Solution
If we attack this by using average as the total score divided by the total number of games, we get the solution.

Mary's average was 177 for an unknown number of games, say x games.

Then her total score was $177x$.

She then bowled 1 game of 199 so her total score is $177x + 199$ for $x + 1$ games.

But this average is 178, so $\dfrac{177x + 199}{x + 1} = 178$

$$177x + 199 = 178x + 178$$
$$x = 21.$$

She has bowled 21 games with an average of 177 and 1 game with a score of 199.

What must she score in her twenty-third game to maintain an average of 179?

If she scores y on her next game her total score is $21 \times 177 + 1 \times 199 + 1 \times y$ and this is accomplished in 23 games so $\dfrac{21 \times 177 + 1 \times 199 + 1 \times y}{23} = 179.$

$$3717 + 199y = 23 \times 179$$
$$= 4117 - 3717 - 999$$
$$= 201.$$

She must bowl 201 in her twenty-third game.

Let us try again using a more simplistic approach.

Mary rolled $199 - 177 = 22$ points above her average and this increased her average by 1.

Therefore she must have bowled 22 games, 1 above her average for the 22 games.

In her next game (her 23rd) she wants to raise her average 1 more point, so she must score 23 more points, 1 for each of her games.

Thus she must score $178 + 23 = 201$.

Her twenty-third game score is 201.

Number Patterns

The use of number patterns is another valuable tool in problem solving.

We have already seen this in an example such as evaluating $1 - 3 + 5 - 7 + 9 - 11 + ...$ to a sum of 50 terms. For example, if you are asked to evaluate 50 terms of the sequence 6, 4, – 2, 6, ..., where each term, t_n, after the first two terms, is derived by finding $t_{n-1} - t_{n-2}$, how do you proceed?

Continue writing the sequence, using the given rule, and you find it is 6, 4, – 2, – 6, – 4, 2, 6, 4, – 2, – 6, ...

Now the pattern becomes apparent and you can sum the sequence to any number of terms.

This is enough discussion. It is time for you to try the problems that have been accumulated for you. Their solutions depend on some of the things that have been discussed. You will find that the use of simple arithmetic often enhances the solution to problems.

Problems

1. Find the value of $16 - 14(16 - 14)$.

2. Find the value of $2\frac{1}{10} + 3\frac{11}{100} + 4\frac{111}{1000}$.

3. Find the value of $\dfrac{\frac{3}{7} - 1}{1 - \frac{7}{3}}$.

4. In the subtraction question $\begin{array}{r} 4\ \heartsuit\ 7 \\ -\ 1\ 8\ 9 \\ \hline 2\ 6\ 8 \end{array}$, what digit does the $\heartsuit$ symbol represent?

5. A number was doubled and then increased by 12. The result was then tripled, giving an answer of 96. What was the original number?

6. The five integers 3, 4, 8, 15, and 19 are rearranged so that the sum of the first three integers equals the sum of the last three integers. What is the middle integer in the rearrangement?

7. Find the value of $(1)^{10} + (-1)^8 + (-1)^7 + (1)^5$.

8. Find the value of $\sqrt{3^2 + 4^2 + 12^2}$.

9. Find the value of $\sqrt{7 + \sqrt{4}}$.

10. When 24 is added to a number, the number is tripled. What is the original number?

11. What is the value of $3^2 \times 3^3 \times 3^4$ written as a power of 3; of 9; of 27?

12. Find the value of $\left(12.5 \times 10^{-3}\right) \times \left(8 \times 10^{111}\right)$ expressed as a power of 10.

13. If $\sqrt{x+9} = 9$, find the value of x.

14. What is the value of x such that $\frac{8}{15} + \frac{7}{30} = \frac{x}{30}$?

15. Find the value of $4^{31} \div 8^{17}$.

16. If $\left(3^a\right)\left(3^b\right)\left(3^c\right) = 243$, find the average of a, b, and c.

17. Find the number of integers between $-\sqrt{10}$ and $\sqrt{110}$.

18. Find the largest prime number that divides 1995 exactly.

19. What is the sum of the reciprocals of the positive divisors of 6?

20. A machine can stamp 50 letters in a minute. If it is operated at the same rate, how many seconds are required to stamp 80 letters?

21. Sandy bought a mint-condition stamp and sold it to Chris, making a profit of $5.00. Chris sold it to Rafeena and lost $2.00. Rafeena made a profit of $4.00 by selling it to Athos for $21.00. What price did Sandy pay for the stamp?

22. If k is an integer and $\frac{k}{30}$ is between $\frac{1}{3}$ and $\frac{2}{5}$, what is the value of k?

23. If $10 \le x \le 20$ and $40 \le y \le 60$, find the largest value of $\frac{x^2}{2y}$.

24. If two numbers are selected from $-9, -7, -5, 2, 4$, and 6, and then multiplied together, what is the least possible value of this product?

25. Chris and Pat are planning a meal together. Chris spends $8.43 at one grocery store and $13.37 at another. At a third store, Pat bought $2.46 worth of groceries. If the cost of the dinner is to be split evenly, how much does Pat owe Chris?

26. A piggy bank holds $5.64 consisting of pennies, nickels, dimes, quarters, and dollar coins. If there is an equal number of coins of each kind, what is the total number of coins in the bank?

27. Janet has 10 coins consisting of nickels, dimes, and quarters. Seven of the coins are either dimes or quarters, and eight of the coins are either dimes or nickels. How many dimes does Janet have?

28. Cathy started with $4.50 and Amy with $3.00. Cathy spent twice as much as Amy, and now discovers she has only one-half as much money as Amy has. What was the total amount of money spent by both girls?

29. On each application of CMC weed spray, 80% of the weeds are killed. In Dan D. Lion's test plot there are 275 weeds. After Dan has sprayed the plot twice, what is the number of weeds remaining?

30. During 1996, the population of Sudbury decreased by 6% while the population of Victoria increased by 14%. At the end of 1996, the populations of these cities were equal. What was the ratio of the population of Sudbury to the population of Victoria at the beginning of 1996?

31. A jar is filled with a mixture of water and vinegar in the ratio 2:1. Another jar, with twice the volume, is filled with a mixture of water and vinegar in the ratio 3:1. If the contents of both jars are emptied into a third container, find the ratio of water to vinegar in this mixture.

32. If the sum of nine consecutive positive integers is 99, what is the largest of these integers?

33. The number 35 805 is the product of three consecutive odd integers. Find the average of these three integers.

34. The average of eight numbers is 5. One of the numbers is increased making the average 6. By how much is the one number increased?

35. The average of a set of twenty numbers is 36. The numbers 38 and 52 are removed from the set. What is the average of the remaining numbers?

36. How many of the integers between 2 and 50 can be written in the form x^y, where x and y are positive integers and $y \neq 1$?

37. If $x^2yz^3 = 7^3$ and $xy^2 = 7^9$, find the numerical value of xyz.

38. If $3^x + 2^y = 995$ and $3^x - 2^y = 473$, find the value of $x + y$.

39. Find the value of $\dfrac{2^{1990} - 2^{1989}}{2^{1990} + 2^{1989}}$.

40. We are given that $(x+y)^2 = 16$, $(y+z)^2 = 36$, and $(z+x)^2 = 81$. If $x+y+z > 3$, find the possible values for $x+y+z$.

41. If $6^{x+2} - 6^x = 210\sqrt{6}$, find the numerical value of 6^{2x-1}.

42. If $2^{6.5} = a$ and $3^{7.5} = b$, find the value of $6^{9.5}$ in terms of a and b.

43. Find the smallest positive integer by which $2^9 \times 3^{14} \times 5^{15} \times 6^3$ must be multiplied to form a perfect square.

44. List 3^{666}, 4^{555}, 5^{444}, 6^{333} and 7^{222} in descending order of magnitude.

45. The sum of the first 50 positive odd integers is 50^2. What is the sum of the first 50 positive even integers?

46. In the sequence 6, 14, 8, -6, ... every term after the second is the difference of the preceding two terms in reverse order. For example, $8 = 14 - 6$ and $-6 = 8 - 14$. Find the sum of the first 2000 terms of this sequence.

Chapter 3   *Perimeter, Area, Volume*

In this section we shall discuss a variety of problems on perimeter, area, and volume. We assume that you know formulas for the perimeters and areas of squares, rectangles, and circles, as well as a formula for the volume of a rectangular box.

Since the number π occurs frequently when working with circles, some historical background has been included.

At the end of the section we have added a short list of formulas that may be useful in solving the problems.

Perimeter

A regular n-gon is a closed figure with n sides of equal length, and with equal angles at each vertex. The perimeter of a regular n-gon is $n \times$ (the length of one side), since all sides have equal length. For example, the perimeter of a regular decagon, with side length 7 cm, is $7 \times 10 = 70$ cm.

The perimeter of any triangle is the sum of the lengths of its three sides. For certain special triangles some of these lengths are the same. What kinds of triangles have equal side lengths?

If a triangle is right-angled, then the famous *Pythagorean Theorem* gives us a very useful relationship for finding the length of a side.

Let a, b, and c be the sides of a right angled triangle (c is the hypotenuse). Then the Pythagorean Theorem says that $a^2 + b^2 = c^2$.

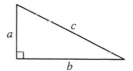

Example 1

In the diagram, if P, Q, R, and S lie in a straight line, what is the perimeter of the figure?

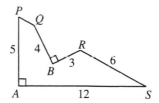

Solution

In order to find the perimeter, we must find the length of PQ; all other lengths are given.

Since P, Q, R, and S lie in a straight line, they all lie along the hypotenuse of right-angled triangle PAS.

Using the Pythagorean Theorem,

$$(PS)^2 = (PA)^2 + (AS)^2$$
$$= (5)^2 + (12)^2$$
$$= 169.$$
$$PS = \sqrt{169} = 13.$$

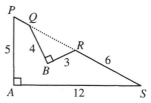

In order to find the length of PQ, we must subtract the lengths of QR and RS from PS. Again, notice that QR is the hypotenuse of right-angled triangle QRB.

Then $(QR)^2 = (QB)^2 + (BR)^2$

$$= 4^2 + 3^2$$
$$= 25.$$
$$QR = 5.$$

The length of PQ is $13 - (5 + 6) = 2$ and the perimeter of the figure is $5 + 12 + 6 + 3 + 4 + 2 = 32$ units.

In order to calculate the perimeter (circumference) of a circle, we need to know the radius. The circumference, C, is given by $C = 2\pi r$ units, where π is the irrational number (non-repeating, non-terminating decimal) approximated by 3.14. Later in this section we'll take a brief look at the number π and its relationship with circles.

Can we calculate a portion of the circumference of a circle (an arc length)?

We need to know what fraction of the entire circumference to calculate, which means we need to know the angle θ at the centre of the circle. Since the circumference of a circle is associated with $360°$ (a full revolution), then an arc length associated with angle θ is $\dfrac{\theta}{360}$ of the entire circumference or $S = \dfrac{\theta}{360}(2\pi r)$.

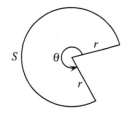

Example 2
A circular piece of paper with radius 10 cm has a sector removed, as shown in the diagram. The resulting piece of paper is formed into a drinking cup in the shape of a cone.
(a)   What is the circumference of the circular top of the drinking cup?
(b)   What is the radius of the cup?
(c)   What is the height of the cup?

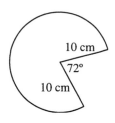

Solution
If we picture the cup that has been formed, we can relate the measurements of the original piece of paper to measurements of the cup.
(If it helps, cut a circle from a piece of paper, cut out a sector of the circle and then join to form a cone).

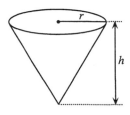

(a)   When the piece of paper is joined to form a cone, the arc length of the circular piece of paper becomes the circumference of the top of the cone.

Since a piece of the circle with angle $72°$ was removed from the circle, then the angle at the centre of the remaining piece is $360° - 72° = 288°$.

The arc length of the original piece of paper is $\frac{288}{360}(2\pi(10)) = \frac{4}{5}(20\pi)$

$$= 16\pi.$$

Thus the circumference of the circular top of the cone is 16π.

(b)   Since we know the circumference of the top of the cup, we can find its radius, r.

$$2\pi r = 16\pi$$
$$r = 8.$$

The radius of the cone is 8 cm.

(c)   To find the height of the cone, notice that the height, radius, and slant height of the cone (distance from point to circumference) are the lengths of a right-angled triangle. Notice also that when the original piece of paper is shaped into the cone, the circle radius of 10 cm becomes the slant height.

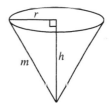

Then $r^2 + h^2 = m^2$

$$8^2 + h^2 = 10^2$$
$$h^2 = 36$$
$$h = 6.$$

The height of the cone is 6 cm.

The number π

Ancient mathematicians discovered that, for any circle, the ratio of its circumference to its diameter was a fixed number which we call π. Efforts to compute the value of π have been going on for over 2000 years. We will briefly describe several methods.

Around 240 B.C., Archimedes used regular inscribed and circumscribed polygons to approximate a value for π. He began with a circle of diameter 1 and circumference $\pi(1) = \pi$. He inscribed and circumscribed regular hexagons around the circle and found their perimeters. These provided lower and upper bounds for the value of π.

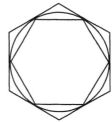

Example 3

For a circle of diameter 1 unit, find

(a)   the perimeter of a regular inscribed hexagon;

(b)   the perimeter of a regular circumscribed hexagon;

(c)   upper and lower bounds for the value of π.

Solution

(a)   Since the diameter of the circle is 1, the radius is $\frac{1}{2}$.

Also, since the hexagon is regular, it can be divided into 6 equilateral triangles, as shown. Since each triangle has side lengths $\frac{1}{2}$, the inscribed hexagon has perimeter

$$6\left(\tfrac{1}{2}\right)=3.$$

(b)   Once again, divide the hexagon into six equilateral triangles, as shown. The radius is now the altitude of any of these triangles.

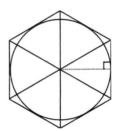

Since the triangles are equilateral, the altitude divides the base in half. If we let the length of a side of this triangle be x, then we find

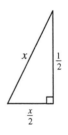

$$\left(\tfrac{1}{2}\right)^2+\left(\tfrac{x}{2}\right)^2=x^2$$

$$1+x^2=4x^2$$

$$x^2=\tfrac{1}{3}$$

$$x=\tfrac{1}{\sqrt{3}}.$$

Therefore the perimeter of the circumscribed hexagon is $\dfrac{6}{\sqrt{3}}=2\sqrt{3}$.

(c)   The circumference of the circle is larger than the perimeter of the inscribed hexagon but smaller than the perimeter of the circumscribed hexagon. Since the circumference of the circle is $\pi(1)$,

we get $3<\pi(1)<2\sqrt{3}$

or $3<\pi<3.4641.$

These bounds for π are not very accurate.

Archimedes was able to improve these upper and lower bounds by using regular polygons with more sides. Using polygons of 96 sides, he was able to show that
$$\frac{223}{71} < \pi < \frac{22}{7}.$$
This gives π accurate to 2 decimal places; that is, $\pi \doteq 3.14$.

Almost 2000 years later, in 1610 A.D., Ludolph van Ceulen of the Netherlands used Archimedes' method with polygons of 2^{62} sides! He was able to compute π to thirty-five decimal places. Since he spent such a large part of his life on this task, when he died his wife had the number engraved on his tombstone!

Around 1671, the Scottish mathematician James Gregory found the infinite series
$$\pi = 4 - \frac{4}{3} + \frac{4}{5} - \frac{4}{7} + \frac{4}{9} - \dots .$$
It takes many terms in this series to compute π to even a few decimal places of accuracy. You should evaluate the sum of the first ten terms on your calculator and see what result you get.

In 1737, Euler began to use the symbol π to represent the ratio of the circumference of a circle to its diameter. It was not until 1767 that Johann Heinrich Lambert showed that π is irrational. Many more calculations for π were done using infinite series, the most accurate being the 707 decimal places found by William Shanks of England in 1873. With the advent of computers, π has been computed to over 2 000 000 decimal places. You can even find such computations on the Internet.

For those of you that have difficulty remembering a value of π to use for approximations, keep the following phrase in mind: "May I have a large container of coffee?" (Replace each word by the number of letters it contains!)

Area
You already know how to find the areas of simple figures such as squares, rectangles, triangles, and circles. Most of the additional figures we consider will have areas that are based on these few basic ones.

The area of a parallelogram of base b and height h, (measured perpendicular to the base), is $b \times h$. We can verify this by removing a right triangle from one side of the parallelogram and joining it to the other end, creating a rectangle of width h, length b, and area $b \times h$.

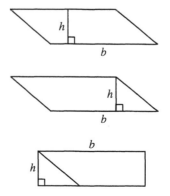

It is important to note that if a figure is cut into pieces and rearranged into a different figure, the area remains constant; that is, the area does not change.

Example 4
A rectangle of width 9 and length 16 is cut along the
dotted lines shown and the pieces are rearranged to form
a square. What is the perimeter of the square?

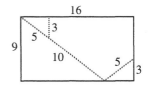

Solution
Although at first glance this looks like a perimeter problem, it really requires us to realize that
when the rectangle is cut and the pieces are rearranged, the area remains the same. (Notice that
the perimeter will change, as some of the outside edges become inside edges, and vice versa).

The area of the rectangle is $9 \times 16 = 144$ square units.
The square also has an area of 144 square units.
Thus the side length of the square is 12 units, and its perimeter is $4 \times 12 = 48$ units.

Example 5
A square with area 100 cm^2 is inscribed in a semicircle. What is the area of a square that could
be inscribed in the entire circle?

Solution
Sketch a diagram of both situations.
Let the radius be r.
Since the square inscribed in the semicircle has area
100 cm^2, its sides are 10 cm in length. In the first
diagram, join OA. Since OA is a radius, it has length r.
By symmetry of both the semicircle and the square,
$OB = \frac{1}{2}(10) = 5$.

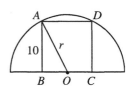

Since ABO is a right-angled triangle,

$$r^2 = 10^2 + 5^2$$
$$= 125.$$
$$r = \sqrt{125}$$
$$= 5\sqrt{5}.$$

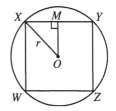

Thus the radii of both the semicircle and the circle are $5\sqrt{5}$ cm.

In the second diagram, draw OM perpendicular to XY and join OX. Since OX is a radius, it has
length $5\sqrt{5}$ cm.
Let the side length of the inscribed square be $2k$ cm. (We choose $2k$ to avoid fractions).
By symmetry, $XM = OM = k$.

Since XMO is a right-angled triangle, $k^2 + k^2 = \left(5\sqrt{5}\right)^2$

$$2k^2 = 125.$$

The area of the square inscribed in the entire circle is $(2k)^2 = 4k^2 = 250 \text{ cm}^2$.

To find the area of a sector of a circle, we use a process similar to the one used for finding arc length; that is, we first determine what fraction of an entire circle the sector represents, then we take that fraction of the area of the circle.

Example 6
Find the surface area of the outside of the cone-shaped drinking cup in Example 2.

Solution
We know that when the drinking cup is flattened, it is a sector of a circle of radius 10 cm. We also know that the sector angle is $288°$.

Thus, the area of the sector is $\frac{288}{360}\left(\pi \times 10^2\right) = \frac{4}{5}(100\pi)$

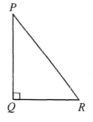

$$= 80\pi$$

$$\doteq 240 \text{ cm}^2.$$

This is the same as the surface area of the outside of the drinking cup.

Example 7
In the diagram, $\angle PQR = 90°$ and $QR = 8$ cm.
If the area of $\triangle PQR$ is 40 cm^2, find the length of PR.

Solution
Since the area of $\triangle PQR$ is 40 cm^2, $\frac{1}{2}(QR)(PQ) = 40$

$$\frac{1}{2}(8)(PQ) = 40$$

$$PQ = 10.$$

Thus PQ has length 10 cm and, using the Pythagorean Theorem, we get $(PR)^2 = 8^2 + 10^2$

$$PR = \sqrt{164} \text{ cm}.$$

There are other situations in which it is possible to find the area of a triangle without knowing a base and a height. In the special case of an equilateral triangle, we can find a formula for the area that depends only on the side length of the triangle.

Consider equilateral triangle ABC with sides of length $2x$. Draw a perpendicular from A meeting BC at D. Since $\triangle ABC$ is equilateral, $BD = DC = x$.

In $\triangle ABD$, $AD^2 = AB^2 - BD^2$

$$= 4x^2 - x^2$$

$$= 3x^2.$$

$$AD = \sqrt{3}x.$$

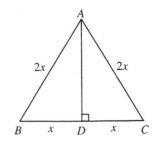

The area of $\triangle ABC$ is $\frac{1}{2}(2x)\sqrt{3}x = \sqrt{3}x^2$.

Heron of Alexandria, who lived in the first century A.D., derived a formula for the area of a triangle in terms of the lengths of its three sides.

Heron's formula is $\Delta = \sqrt{s(s-a)(s-b)(s-c)}$, where Δ represents the area of the triangle with sides a, b, and c, and where s is the semi-perimeter of the triangle, that is, $s = \dfrac{a+b+c}{2}$.

No altitude measurements are required for this calculation. Notice that for an equilateral triangle of side length $2x$ the semiperimeter is $s = \dfrac{6x}{2} = 3x$. Heron's formula gives the area as

$$\sqrt{3x(x)(x)(x)} = \sqrt{3x^4}$$

$$= \sqrt{3}x^2.$$

This is the same as the result we found above in the previous problem.

Example 8
Find the area of a triangle with sides of lengths 7, 8, and 11.

Solution
The semi-perimeter is $s = \dfrac{7+8+11}{2} = 13$.

The area is $\sqrt{13(13-7)(13-8)(13-11)} = \sqrt{13 \times 6 \times 5 \times 2}$

$$= \sqrt{780}$$

$$\doteq 28.$$

When you study trigonometry and linear algebra, you will come across more ways to compute the area of a triangle.

A trapezoid is a four-sided figure in which one pair of opposite sides are parallel.

The area of a trapezoid is given by $\frac{1}{2}(s_1 + s_2)(h)$, where s_1 and s_2 are the lengths of the two parallel sides and h is the perpendicular distance between these sides.

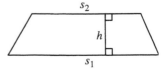

We will now use this formula to help us prove a well known theorem.

Consider right-angled triangle MQN with side lengths a, b, and c.

Draw congruent triangle PRN as shown in the diagram.

Note that $\angle MNP = 90°$. (You should be able to explain why this is so).

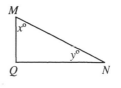

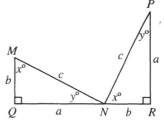

Join PM. The resulting figure is trapezoid $MQRP$, with parallel sides PR and MQ, and height QR.

We will find the area of this trapezoid in two ways; by using the trapezoid formula and by adding the areas of the three right-angled triangles that make up the trapezoid.

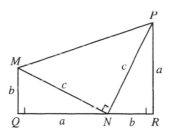

Thus, $\frac{1}{2}(MQ + PR)(QR) = \frac{1}{2}(MQ)(QN) + \frac{1}{2}(NR)(RP) + \frac{1}{2}(MN)(NP)$

$$(a+b)(a+b) = ab + ab + c^2$$
$$a^2 + 2ab + b^2 = 2ab + c^2$$
$$a^2 + b^2 = c^2.$$

Since a, b, and c are the lengths of the sides of a right-angled triangle, we have just proved the Pythagorean Theorem.

If you recall that the square of a number x is the same as the area of a square of side length x, the Pythagorean Theorem can be interpreted as illustrated in the diagram. If a, b, and c are the sides of a right-angled triangle, with c being the hypotenuse, then the sum of the areas of the squares with side lengths a and b, respectively, is equal to the area of a square having side length c.

That is, $a^2 + b^2 = c^2$.

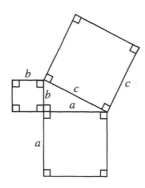

Suppose we draw semicircles on the sides of a right-
angled triangle, as shown. You can prove that the area of
the semicircle on the hypotenuse is equal to the sum of
the areas of the semicircles drawn on the other two sides
(try it).

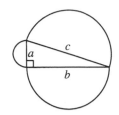

Try to prove the same result for equilateral triangles
drawn on the sides of a right-angled triangle.
Do you think you can generalize these results?

Area can be measured for three-dimensional objects, as well as those in two dimensions. In three
dimensions, area is usually referred to as surface area.

The surface area of a rectangular box of dimensions x, y,
and z is the sum of the areas of the six rectangles that
make up the box. Since pairs of these rectangles are
congruent, the surface area is $2xy + 2yz + 2xz$.

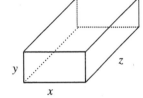

For a cylinder of radius r and height h, the surface area
may or may not include the circular ends.

Each end has area πr^2.

To find the area of the side of the cylinder, we cut it and
open it flat to form a rectangle.

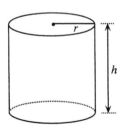

This rectangle has height h. Its width is the
circumference of a circle of radius r, which is $2\pi r$.
The area of the rectangle and thus of the side of the cylinder
is $2\pi rh$.

Volume
Volume is a measure of three-dimensional space, and is
measured in cubic units.
The boundaries of this space may be flat or curved.
The volume of a rectangular box of dimensions x, y, and
z is the product xyz.

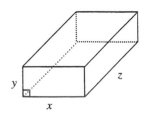

Example 9
The volume of a cube, in cm^3, is equal to its surface area, in cm^2. What is the total length of all
of the edges of the cube?

Solution

Let the length of one side of the cube be x cm. The volume of this cube is x^3. The surface area of the cube is made up of the areas of six squares, each of side length x. Thus the surface area is $6x^2$.

Since the volume and the surface area are the same number, (different units of measure), then

$$x^3 = 6x^2$$
$$x^3 - 6x^2 = 0$$
$$x^2(x - 6) = 0.$$

$x = 0$ or $x = 6$.   ($x = 0$ is inadmissible)

The length of one side of the cube is 6 cm. Since a cube has 12 edges, the total length of all the edges of the cube is $12(6) = 72$ cm.

The volume of a cylinder of radius r and height h is $\pi r^2 h$. Notice that this is the product of the area of the bottom (a circle with area πr^2) and the height.

In fact, the volume of any right prism can be calculated as (area of bottom face) $\times$ height. (A right prism is a solid in which the top and bottom faces are congruent shapes, and the sides are at right angles to both top and bottom).

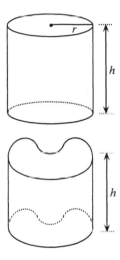

The volume of a right circular cone of radius r and height h is $\frac{1}{3}\pi r^2 h$. (That is, it would take 3 cones full of water to fill a cylinder of the same radius and height. You may want to try this yourself as an experiment).

Example 10

Find the volume of the drinking cup from Example 2.

Solution

A circular piece of paper of radius 10 cm has had a sector removed and then been folded to form a drinking cup in the shape of a right circular cone.

In Example 2, we found that the radius of this cone is 8 cm and the height is 6 cm.

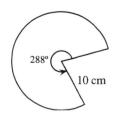

The volume of the drinking cup is $\frac{1}{3}\pi(8)^2(6) = 128\pi$ cm^3.

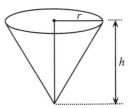

A Few Useful Formulas

- Area of a triangle with sides a, b, and c

  $$A = \frac{1}{2}ah$$

  $$= \frac{1}{2}ab \sin C$$

  $$= \sqrt{s(s-a)(s-b)(s-c)}, \text{ where } s = \frac{a+b+c}{2}.$$

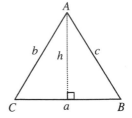

- Surface area of an sphere

  $$s = 4\pi r^2.$$

- Area of an ellipse

  $$A = \pi ab.$$

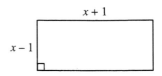

- Volume of a square-based pyramid

  $$V = \frac{1}{3}a^2 h.$$

- Volume of a sphere

  $$V = \frac{4}{3}\pi r^3.$$

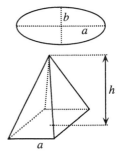

Problems

1. If the perimeter of the given rectangle is 24, what is the value of x?

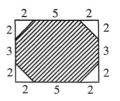

2. In the 9 by 7 rectangle shown, what is the area of the shaded region?

3. If the area of a square is 484 cm^2, what is its perimeter?

4. If the radius of a circle is increased by 5 units, what is the ratio of the new circumference to the new diameter?

5. The circumference of a circle, in cm, is equal to its area, in cm². What is the radius of the circle?

6. A set of *n* circles, each with a diameter of 1 cm, has a total area equal to that of a circle with radius 3 cm. What is the value of *n*?

7. In each row and each column of the diagram, the points are spaced one unit apart. What is the area of the shaded region?

8. Three small rectangles, of the same depth, are cut from a rectangular sheet of metal. The area of the remaining piece is 990. What is the depth of each cut?

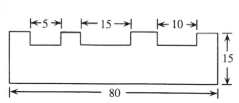

9 Rectangle *PQRS*, with area 150, is divided into two congruent squares and two congruent rectangles as shown. If the smaller rectangles are each twice as long as they are wide, find the perimeter of rectangle *PQRS*.

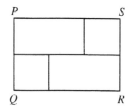

10. Ruby has 131 identical cubes. She uses these to build a solid cube, using as many of the 131 cubes as possible. How many of them will be left over?

11. What is the area of convex quadrilateral *ABCD*?

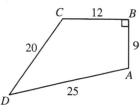

12. In the diagram, the length of each side of the smaller square is one-half the length of each side of the larger square. What is the ratio of the shaded area to the area of the larger square?

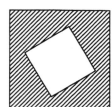

13. *P* is the centre of square *WXYZ* and *R* is the
     midpoint of *WZ*. If the area of △*XPR* is 3, find
     the shaded area.

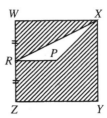

14. One wall of a building measures 20 m by 60 m. It has 20 windows, each measuring 2 m
     by 3 m. What percentage of the wall is made up by windows?

15. Triangle *PQR* has an area of *x*. If the lengths of
     the sides are *p*, *q*, and *r*, what is the length of the
     altitude from *P*?

16. The area of square *ACEG* is 121. The area of
     square *ABJH* is 81. What is the area of square
     KJIL?

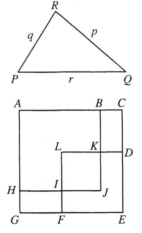

17. The volume of a fish tank is 20 litres. A new tank is constructed with each of its
     dimensions twice those of the original tank. Find the volume of the larger tank.

18. In the diagram adjacent edges are at right angles.
     The four longer edges are equal in length, and all of
     the shorter edges are also equal in length. If the
     area of the shape is 528, what is the perimeter?

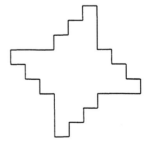

19. A round pizza of radius 20 cm and uniform thickness of 2 cm is reshaped before cooking to
     form a square. If the square pizza has a uniform thickness of 1 cm, what is the length of one
     of its sides, to the nearest cm?

20. The volume of a cube, in cm³, is equal to its surface area, in cm². What is the total
     length of all the edges?

21. In the given diagram, $PQ \perp QR$, $PS = SR = 5$, and $PQ = 4$. What is the length of PR?

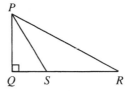

22. In a rectangle, if the sum of the squares of the four sides is 18, what is the length of a diagonal?

23. A metrestick leans against a vertical wall. The foot of the metrestick is 28 cm from the base of the wall. If the top of the metrestick slips 16 cm down the wall, find the distance that the foot of the metrestick will slide.

24. A paperweight is formed by slicing a sphere of radius 26 cm with a straight cut at a distance of 10 cm from the centre of the sphere. What is the circumference of the base of the paperweight?

25. A closed rectangular box 6 cm by 9 cm by 30 cm has the same surface area as a cube. What is the length of an edge of this cube, to the nearest centimetre?

26. The water surface of a swimming pool is a rectangle 10 m wide and 15 m long. The pool is 1 m deep at the shallow end and the depth increases at a constant rate to 3 m deep at the other end. When the pool is full, what is the volume of the water?

27. Four pipes, each of radius r, are tied together with a band as in diagram X with the centres forming the vertices of a square. Four other identical pipes are tied as in figure Y. What is the difference in the lengths of the bands?

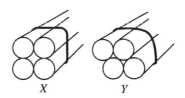

X   Y

28. In the diagram, all triangles are equilateral. If $AB = 16$, what is the total area of all the black triangles?

"Sierpinski Gasket"

29. A glass cylinder with an internal radius of 1 cm contains water to a depth of 2 cm. Three heavy spheres, each of radius 1 cm, are dropped into the cylinder. Find the new location of the surface of the water.

30. $ABCD$ and $XYCZ$ are squares. The area inside square $ABCD$, but outside square $XYCZ$ is 30. If $DY = 10$, what is the length of CD?

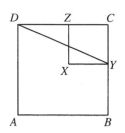

31. $ABCD$ is a rectangle, $EF \perp FB$. If $AE = 2$, $ED = 4$, and $DF = x$, $x > 25$, find the area of triangle BEF.

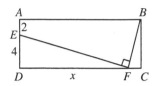

32. The radius of the inscribed circle of a triangle is given by the formula $r = \dfrac{\Delta}{s}$ where Δ is the area of the triangle and s is the semi-perimeter. Find the area of the inscribed circle of a triangle whose sides are 24, 21, and 15 centimetres.

33. $\triangle PQR$ has side QP extended to X so that $QP = PX$, PR extended to Z so that $PR = RZ$, and RQ extended to Y so that $RQ = QY$. If the area of $\triangle XYZ$ is 420, find the area of $\triangle PQR$.

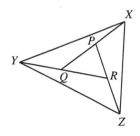

34. If the cross-section of a greenhouse roof is in the shape of a segment of a circle with the dimensions given, what area of plastic is needed to cover the roof and both end walls?

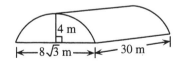

35. A space-station is in the shape of a cube, each of whose edges is of length s. An astronaut working on the outer surface is anchored by means of a rope which allows him to reach a distance s from the anchor point. Calculate the surface area of the station (in terms of s), accessible to the astronaut, if the anchor is located:

(a)   at one corner of the cube.

(b)   in the centre of one face.

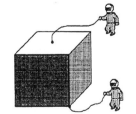

Chapter 4   Triangles, Polygons, Circles

Geometry, from the Greek words *gē*, "earth", and *met'ron*, "measure", was one of the first branches of mathematics to be developed. It remains vitally important today as a way of modelling the shapes that occur in nature. The Babylonians and Egyptians were concerned mainly with applying geometric properties of measurement to agriculture and architecture. The Greeks took this early form of geometry and developed a systematic approach to the subject based on logic in which new facts could be deduced from previously known results.

While geometry is important as a way of modelling the world around us, it is also an intriguing subject to investigate because of its visual nature and the overwhelming sense of beauty and order in the properties of simple shapes.

In this chapter, we will discuss geometry problems based on the properties of congruent triangles, angles in polygons, and chords and tangents of circles.

Triangles
A triangle is the simplest polygon yet has many useful properties. A triangle has three sides and three interior angles. In many geometric problems, it is required to determine equality of line segments or angles or both. When such problems have diagrams that include more than one triangle, the results can often be deduced if the triangles are congruent.

To motivate our discussion, consider the following example.

Example 1
Point K is on side AB of square $ABCD$ and point L is on side BC so that $\angle DKL = \angle DKA$. Point N is on KL such that DN is perpendicular to KL. If $KN = 6$ and $NL = 4$, determine the side length of the square.

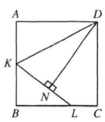

Discussion
Since the lengths of line segments KN and NL are given, it seems likely that the diagram contains other line segments equal to them which, when found, would lead to determining the side length of the square. As we can see, the diagram includes several triangles and if we can deduce pairs of congruent triangles, the result may follow.

Two triangles are said to be congruent if they are equal in all respects. That is, corresponding sides and angles of congruent triangles are equal. Conversely, if the corresponding sides and angles of two triangles are equal, then the triangles are congruent.

It turns out that it is not necessary to have all six of these equalities in order that the triangles be congruent. There are *four* situations in which having three of these six equalities is sufficient to establish congruency.

Triangle Congruency Theorems

1.   If two sides and the contained angle of one triangle are respectively equal to two sides and the contained angle of another triangle, the triangles are congruent.

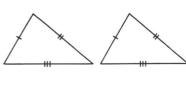

2.   If the three sides of one triangle are respectively equal to the three sides of another triangle, the triangles are congruent.

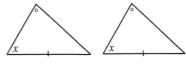

3.   If two angles and a side of one triangle are respectively equal to two angles and the corresponding side of another triangle, the triangles are congruent.

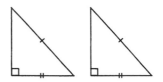

4.   If the hypotenuse and one side of one right-angled triangle are respectively equal to the hypotenuse and one side of another right-angled triangle, the triangles are congruent.

Being able to establish that two triangles are congruent enables us to conclude further equalities of sides and angles in those triangles.

We now proceed to solve Example 1.

Solution

Since $ABCD$ is a square, the side length s equals $AK + KB$. Since $\angle DAK = \angle DNK = 90°$, $\angle AKD = \angle NKD$, and KD is common to both triangles, then triangle ADK is congruent to triangle NDK.

Hence $AK = NK = 6$, and $DA = DN$.

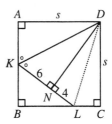

We have used the given information that $KN = 6$. It is not immediately obvious how to use the fact that $NL = 4$.

Joining strategic points in a diagram often leads to further progress in the solution of a problem. In this case, the symmetry within quadrilateral $DNLC$ suggests that we join DL.

Since $DN = DC$ and DL is a common hypotenuse, triangle DNL is congruent to triangle DCL. Hence $NL = LC = 4$.

Since $AB = BC = s$, $KB = s - 6$ and $BL = s - 4$.

In triangle KBL, the Pythagorean Theorem yields

$$KB^2 + BL^2 = KL^2$$
$$(s-6)^2 + (s-4)^2 = 100$$
$$s^2 - 12s + 36 + s^2 - 8s + 16 = 100$$
$$2s^2 - 20s - 48 = 0$$
$$s^2 - 10s - 24 = 0$$
$$(s-12)(s+2) = 0$$
$$s = 12. \quad \text{(Why is } s \ne -2\text{?)}$$

Therefore the side length of the square is 12.

In summary, the key to solving this problem was finding the lengths of AK and LC. Two pairs of congruent triangles enabled us to do so. From there, applying the Pythagorean Theorem to triangle KBL and solving the resulting quadratic equation lead to the answer.

The Isosceles Triangle

An isosceles triangle is a triangle with two of its sides equal in length.
The isosceles triangle has a symmetry which results in some special properties.

Properties of an Isosceles Triangle

*   The angles opposite the equal sides are equal.
*   The median to the base is also an altitude and as a result is the right-bisector of the base.

These properties can be proven using the congruent triangle theorems. The converses of the above statements are also true.

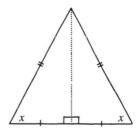

Angles in Polygons

The simplest polygon is a triangle. You probably have known for quite a while that the sum of the three interior angles of any triangle is 180°. One method of proving this result is to use the angle relationships resulting from a transversal meeting two parallel lines.
If a transversal, PQ, meets two parallel lines, then the four angles marked x are equal and the four angles marked y are equal. (The converse is also true.)

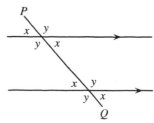

Example 2
Prove that the sum of the interior angles of a triangle is $180°$.

Proof
Through A draw line DAE parallel to BC.

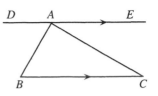

Since $DAE \parallel BC$ and AC is a transversal, $\angle EAC = \angle C$.
Similarly, $\angle DAB = \angle B$.
Hence, $\angle BAC + \angle B + \angle C = \angle BAC + \angle DAB + \angle EAC$
$\qquad\qquad\qquad = 180°$. (DAE is a straight angle)
Thus the sum of the interior angles of a triangle is $180°$.

Example 3
Find the sum of the interior angles of a pentagon.

Discussion
A pentagon is a polygon with five sides. At first, you might see no way to find the sum of the five interior angles. It turns out that all we need to do is partition the pentagon into triangles.

Solution
Choose any point P inside pentagon $ABCDE$ and join it to the five vertices.

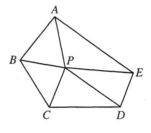

The sum of the angles in each of the triangles is $180°$.
Thus the sum of the angles in all five triangles is
$5 \times 180° = 900°$.
Ten of the fifteen interior angles of the five triangles form the five interior angles of the pentagon. The other five angles at P form a complete rotation of $360°$.
Hence the sum of the interior angles of a pentagon is
$5 \times 180° - 360° = 540°$.

In general, this method can be applied to any polygon.
You might like to prove that the sum of the interior angles of a polygon having n sides is $n \times 180° - 360°$.

A *regular polygon* is a polygon having all its sides equal and all its angles equal.
Thus, if the pentagon in example 3 was a regular pentagon, each of its interior angles would be $\frac{540°}{5} = 108°$.

Definition
The exterior angle at a vertex of a polygon is the angle formed by one side and the extended part of an adjacent side.

Example 4
Find the sum of the exterior angles of a pentagon.

Solution
At each vertex, the sum of the interior and exterior angles
is 180°.
The sum of the five interior and five exterior angles is
$5 \times 180° = 900°$.
Since the five interior angles have a sum of 540°, the sum
of the five exterior angles is $900° - 540° = 360°$.

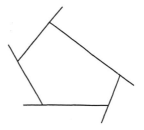

Note: The size of each interior angle of a regular pentagon equals $180° - \dfrac{360°}{5} = 180° - 72° = 108°$.

Circles (Chords and Tangents)
The circle is another simple geometric figure, and yet, because of central symmetry has many
properties that can be helpful in solving problems. In this section we will focus on properties of
chords and tangent lines. To motivate our discussion, consider the following example.

Example 5
A semicircular piece of paper with radius 2 is creased
and folded along a chord so that the arc is tangent to the
diameter as shown in the diagram. If the contact point of
the arc divides the diameter in the ratio 3:1, determine
the length of the crease.

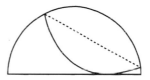

Discussion
The arc of the folded segment creates a situation in which there are parts of two congruent circles
in the diagram. The line segment about which the fold occurred is a chord common to the two
circles and the diameter of the one circle is tangent to the other circle.

In order to proceed with the solution, we first need to recall some properties of circles that relate
the centre of a circle to chords and tangent lines.

Properties of Chords
1. The right bisector of a chord of a circle passes
    through the centre.
2. The perpendicular line from the centre of a circle to
    a chord bisects the chord.
3. The line joining the centre of a circle and the
    mid-point of a chord is perpendicular to the chord.

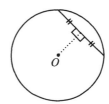

Properties of Tangents

1. A straight line drawn at right angles to a radius of a circle at the circumference is a tangent.
2. The line joining the centre of a circle to the point of contact of a tangent is at right angles to the tangent.
3. A line drawn at right angles to a tangent at the point of contact passes through the centre of the circle.

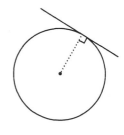

We now proceed to solve the example 5.

Solution

In order to take advantage of the chord and tangent properties of a circle, and to use the given information, add some additional points and lines to the given diagram.

Let the given semi-circle have diameter AB, centre O, and let T be the point of contact of the tangent line.
Let LM be the common chord.
Draw a line at right angles to AB at T. This line will pass through the centre of the "image" circle.
Join O to N, the mid-point of chord LM, and extend it to meet the perpendicular from T at P.
Since N is the mid-point of chord LM, LN is perpendicular to LM.
Since LN is a chord of the image circle, ON extended passes through the centre of the image circle.
Thus P, the point of intersection of the perpendicular from T and ON extended, is the centre of the "image" circle.

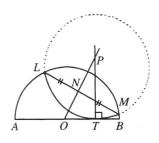

From the given information, $AO = 2$, $OT = TB = 1$.
Since PT is a radius, $PT = 2$.
In right-angled triangle OTP, $OP^2 = 2^2 + 1^2 = 5$.
Thus $OP = \sqrt{5}$.
Since $OL = PL = OM = PM$, LN is the right bisector of OP.

Thus $ON = \frac{\sqrt{5}}{2}$.

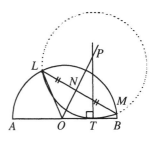

Join O to L.
In right-angled triangle OLN, $OL^2 = ON^2 + LN^2$

$$4 = \frac{5}{4} + LN^2$$

$$LN = \sqrt{\frac{11}{4}}.$$

Thus chord $LM = 2 \times \frac{\sqrt{11}}{2} = \sqrt{11}$.

Therefore the length of the crease is $\sqrt{11}$.

In summary, the key to solving this problem was using the chord and tangent properties of a circle.

With this review of congruent triangles, angles in polygons, and the chord and tangent properties of circles, along with some suggestions as to how they can be applied to solve problems, you are now equipped to solve the problems in this chapter. Enjoy them.

Problems

1. In the diagram, determine the value of *x*.

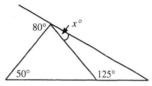

2. In the diagram the triangle shown is isosceles with
    AB = *AC*. Determine the value of *x*.

3. In the diagram, determine the value of *a* + *b*.

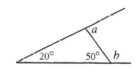

4. In the diagram, *AB* = 4, *DC* = 6, and *AB* is
    parallel to *DC*. If ∠*C* = 45°, determine the
    length of *BD*.

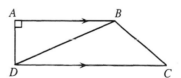

5. Prove that the point of contact of two tangent circles is on the line joining the centres of the two circles.

6. In the diagram, *AB* ∥ *DC*, and *AB* = *BD* = *BC*. If
    ∠*A* = 52°, determine the measure of ∠*DBC*.

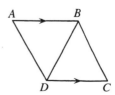

7. Prove that if one pair of opposite sides of a quadrilateral are equal and parallel, then the other pair are equal and parallel.

8. All five of the line segments in the diagram have
    the same length. Determine the measure of
    $\angle ABC$.

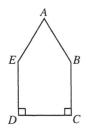

9. Determine the number of different values of a for
    which the given triangle is isosceles.

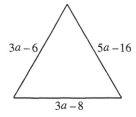

10. A circle has radius 8. A chord of this circle is the perpendicular bisector of a radius.
    Determine the length of the chord.

11. In the diagram, triangle ABC is inscribed in the
    semicircle with centre D. If $AB = AD$, determine
    the measure of angle ACD.

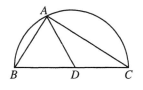

12. A six-pointed star is formed by extending the edges
    of a regular hexagon. If the perimeter of the
    hexagon is 21, what is the perimeter of the star?

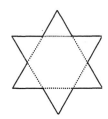

13. In triangle ADC, B is a point on AC such that
    $DA = DB$. If all angles are measured in degrees,
    determine the value of x.

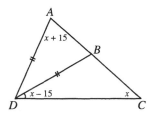

14. Two perpendicular diameters are drawn in a circle of radius 2. All possible chords parallel to and at a distance of 1 unit from these diameters are drawn. What is the sum of the lengths of the six chords in the diagram?

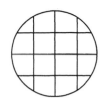

15. A beam of light shines from point S, reflects off a reflector at point P, and reaches point T so that PT is perpendicular to RS. Determine the value of x.

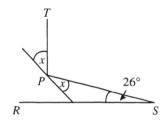

16. In the diagram $AC = BD = DC$ and $\angle ADB = 24°$. Determine the measure of $\angle BDC$.

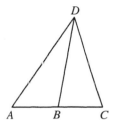

17. Prove that the line which joins the mid-points of two sides of a triangle is parallel to the third side and equal to one-half its length.

18. Prove that the mid-point of the hypotenuse of a right-angled triangle is equidistant from all three vertices.

19. Given triangle ABC as shown, the bisectors of angles ABC and ACB intersect at I. Perpendicular line segments AP and AQ are drawn from the vertex A to lines CI and BI extended. Prove that PQ is parallel to BC.

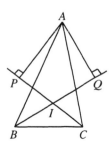

20. XYZ is a triangle with $\angle XZY = 90°$. W is the midpoint of XY, and the circle with diameter ZW intersects WX at V. If $XY = 50$ and $WV = 7$, determine the length of XZ.

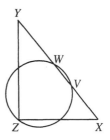

21. Triangle ABC is constructed with $\angle ACB = 120°$ and $\angle CAB = 40°$. AC is extended to P so that $AP = AC + 2CB$. Determine the measure of $\angle ABP$.

22. Prove that the sum of the exterior angles of any polygon is $360°$.

23. The measures, in degrees, of the interior angles of a fifteen-sided polygon are consecutive integers. Determine the measure of the smallest angle.

24. In a convex polygon, exactly five of the interior angles are obtuse. What is the largest possible number of sides for this polygon?

25. A is the centre of a circle which passes through B. B is the centre of a circle which passes through A. CBF and CAE are line segments. If $\angle F = 78°$, determine the measure of $\angle C$.

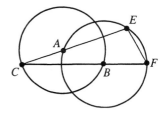

26. Two tangents AT and BT touch a circle at A and B, respectively, and meet perpendicularly at T. Q is on AT, S is on BT, and R is on the circle, such that $QRST$ is a rectangle with $QT = 6$ cm and $ST = 3$ cm. What is the radius of the circle?

27. In a circle with centre O, radius OA is perpendicular to radius OB. A chord is drawn parallel to AB meeting OA at P and OB at Q, and the circle at M and N. If $MP = \sqrt{56}$, and $PN = 12$, determine the length of the radius of the circle.

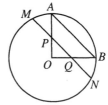

Chapter 5   Analytic Geometry

Modern mathematics began in the seventeenth century when the French mathematician René Descartes successfully demonstrated how to combine geometry and algebra into a consistent mathematical system that could be used to solve both classical and newer problems in mathematics. You will be familiar with some of the fundamental ideas in analytic geometry such as how to algebraically describe points, find the length of a line segment, find the midpoint between two points, and determine the slope of a line. The formulae for these fundamental geometric concepts are reviewed in the chart at the end of this discussion.

Analytic geometry would not, however, have been the beginning of modern mathematics if all that was possible was to deal with the simple geometric ideas described above. There is a story that tells us that Descartes got his inspiration for the creation of his new geometry while lying in bed and watching a spider descend from the ceiling. The legend says that at that point he asked himself the fundamental question: "How can I describe the position of the spider as it moves down the web?" His answer was to create a method for describing the position of a point as it moves through two dimensional space. Descartes' method uses a combination of geometric and algebraic procedures to find an algebraic description of a locus. A *locus* is the path traced out by a moving point. A locus can also be viewed as a set of points (usually an infinite set) located so that each point satisfies some fundamental geometric property. In order to successfully use Descartes' method it is necessary to be able to describe the moving point in some simple geometric manner. The moving point, which creates geometric curves such as straight lines, circles, ellipses, or parabolas, can be described by relating the moving point to some combination of fixed points and lines. You will recall that the formula for any straight line with slope m that passes through a fixed point (x_1, y_1) can be developed by using Descartes' method. Since the locus problem is the fundamental problem of Descartes' analytic geometry it would be appropriate to illustrate the concept with an example.

Example 1
A circle is located on a coordinate system with the centre at the point (2, 3) and with radius 13. Find an algebraic way to describe the position of every point on the circle.

Solution
First it is important to draw the circle in the correct position.

Next, it is necessary to geometrically describe the position of every point on the circle. You will have used a set of compasses to draw circles. Recall that every time you made a drawing the process involved could have been described as follows:

*The **circle** is a set of points located so that every point is the same distance from a fixed point called the centre.*   (1)

To translate this geometric description into algebra we must determine how to algebraically describe the moving point and the distance between the centre and the moving point. This is done as follows:

Let the moving point on the curve be represented
by $P(x, y)$. (2)

Using the distance formula $\sqrt{(x_2 - x_1)^2 + (y_2 - y_1)^2}$, (3)

distance $CP = \sqrt{(x-2)^2 + (y-3)^2}$.

Since it was given that the radius is 13,

we have $\sqrt{(x-2)^2 + (y-3)^2} = 13$.

Square both sides to remove the radical and a simple
form for the algebraic relation that describes all the
points on the circle is the equation

$$(x-2)^2 + (y-3)^2 = 169.$$

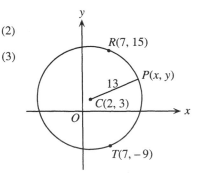

To verify that this equation does indeed produce points that are on the specified circle it is
necessary to substitute appropriate values for x and calculate the corresponding y values. For
example if $x = 7$ then y is either $+15$ or -9. Both these points are on the circle (see points R
and T on the diagram). You can select other x values and test them to find other specific
points. Of course, if the coordinates of a point do not satisfy the equation, the point does not
lie on the circle.

The three important features in Descartes' argument have been numbered. Whenever you
use this procedure you must:
1. Introduce variables x and y to represent the moving point.
2. State a clear geometric definition of the locus.
3. Translate the geometric definition into algebra by using one or more of the basic
   formulas.

In the above example, if the centre and radius are generalized and the argument is repeated, then
the equation for any circle with centre (a, b) and radius r is given by

$$(x-a)^2 + (y-b)^2 = r^2.$$

The reader is invited to work through the proof. This new formula is useful in many problems
where circles are involved. The next example will illustrate one category of problem where the
formula could be used.

Example 2
A circle with centre C on the y-axis passes through the points $A(-3, -1)$ and $B(4, 6)$. Determine
if this circle cuts the straight line defined by the equation $3x - 4y - 13 = 0$.

Solution
Begin with a good diagram so the geometry of the problem can be clearly seen. The centre C of
the circle is located so $|AC| = |BC|$. The straight line appears to be below the circle; however, the
diagram is not accurate enough to be certain this is true. To test the situation with more certainty
it will be necessary to find the algebraic equation for the circle and then find out if the equation for
the line shares any common values with the circle equation. This means the solution will have two
distinct parts.

Part 1

First, we must find the equation of the circle.

Let the centre be $C(0, b)$ located so that $AC = BC$. (1)

Using the formula $\sqrt{(x_2 - x_1)^2 + (y_2 - y_1)^2}$, (1) becomes

$$\sqrt{(0+3)^2 + (b+1)^2} = \sqrt{(0-4)^2 + (b-6)^2}.$$

Square both sides $9 + b^2 + 2b + 1 = 16 + b^2 - 12b + 36$

This simplifies to $14b = 42$

Thus $b = 3$.

Using the above formula, $r = BC = \sqrt{16 + (3-6)^2} = 5$.

Using the equation of a circle formula $(x - a)^2 + (y - b)^2 = r^2$, the equation for this circle is
$(x - 0)^2 + (y - 3)^2 = 5^2$. (2)

Part 2

To establish whether the line intersects the circle, solve equations (2) and (3) This is most easily done by reorganizing the given line equation in the form

$$y = \frac{3x - 13}{4}.$$ (3)

Substitute (3) into (2) to get $x^2 + \dfrac{(3x - 13 - 12)^2}{16} = 25$.

Thus $16x^2 + 9x^2 - 150x + 625 = 400$

$25x^2 - 150x + 225 = 0$

$x^2 - 6x + 9 = 0$

This factors to give $(x - 3)(x - 3) = 0$.

Since both x-values equal 3, this tells us the straight line intersects the circle in a single point at which $x = 3$ and $y = -1$. This type of line is called a *tangent to the circle*.

Observe that the approach to the problem is to transform the geometry into an algebraic format and then work in algebra. Once the algebraic solution is found the geometric interpretation is presented in the concluding sentence. This solution is a good example of the interchange between algebra and geometry that takes place in analytical geometry problems.

Some geometry problems present a geometric condition that is easy to identify, but also contain a second geometric component that is not always obvious to the problem solver. The next example will illustrate a problem of this type.

Example 3

Two lines are defined by the equations $2x - 3y + 6 = 0$ (l_1)

and $5x - 7y - 61 = 0$ (l_2).

Find the point A on the line l_1 so that AB is perpendicular to l_2, where $B(8, -3)$ is on the line l_2.

Solution

Since there must be a right angle at point B, we might   possibly use the relationship for perpendicular lines which says:

If two lines with slopes m_1 and m_2 are perpendicular,

then $m_1 = \dfrac{-1}{m_2}$ or $m_1 m_2 = -1$.   (1)

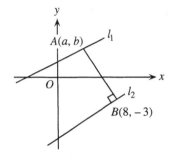

Let the required point A be (a, b).

Slope $AB = \dfrac{-3 - b}{8 - a}$, and the slope of l_2 is $-\dfrac{a}{b} = \dfrac{5}{7}$.

Using (1), we obtain $\dfrac{5}{7} \cdot \dfrac{(-3 - b)}{(8 - a)} = -1$.

Simplify to give $-15 - 5b = -56 + 7a$

$7a + 5b = 41$.   (2)

Now when the variables are defined on the set of real numbers (as they are in this problem) it is usually impossible to obtain a unique answer from a single equation in two variables. This suggests there must be another geometric property on the diagram. Observe that the point A is on the other line. This means the co-ordinates of A must satisfy the equation of l_1.

Substitution of (a, b) in l_1 gives $2a - 3b = -6$.   (3)

The coordinates of the required point must satisfy algebraic conditions (2) and (3). The coordinates can be found by using the method of elimination to solve the system of equations for a and b.

To eliminate b, $3 \times (2)$ gives $21a + 15b = 123$ (4)

$5 \times (3)$ gives $10a - 15b = -30$ (5)

Adding (4) and (5) we get $31a = 93$

$a = 3$.

Substitute in (3) to get $b = 4$.

Therefore the point A is $(3, 4)$.

Note that an alternate approach to this problem would be to find the equation of the line through point B that is perpendicular to l_2. Solve this equation with the equation of the first line and this will give point A. It is left for you to try this approach.

A feature of this problem is that two variables were required to translate the two geometric conditions into algebra. This in turn required that a system of two linear equations in two unknowns had to be solved in order to find the unknown point. Many of the more interesting problems in analytic geometry require two and sometimes three variables. In your problem solving there will be occasions when you do not seem to have enough algebraic information. When this occurs you should study the diagram carefully and ask yourself the question: "Have I used all the geometric conditions that are in this figure?"

One of the most fundamental geometric concepts is area. The chart at the end of Example 4 does not contain an analytical geometry formula for finding areas of simple closed figures. Although a formula exists, it is not usually presented to students in early courses. In the following problems it will be necessary to either use the basic area formula for shapes such as the triangle, circle, rectangle or trapezoid, or it will be necessary to invent some unique approach to find the area. The next example will illustrate both approaches.

Example 4
The straight line with equation $5x - 3y + 33 = 0$ cuts the x-axis at A and the y-axis at B to create triangle AOB. A second triangle RST is defined by points $R(1, 7)$, $S(10, 0)$, and $T(6, 11)$.

(a)   Find the area of $\triangle AOB$.

(b)   Show that the area of $\triangle RST$ is smaller than the area of $\triangle AOB$.

Solution
(a)   To find point A let $y = 0$ in the equation and we get $x = \dfrac{-33}{5}$.

Similarly, for point B, let $x = 0$ in the equation and we get $y = 11$.

Since $\triangle AOB$ is right-angled, the area is given by the formula $A = \dfrac{1}{2}bh$.

Thus, the area of $\triangle AOB = \dfrac{1}{2}\left(\dfrac{33}{5}\right)(11) = 36.3$.

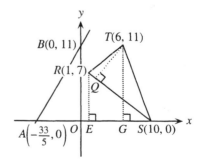

(b)   The sketch suggests that $\triangle RST$ does not have a right angle. It is left to you to use a slope test to verify this observation. Thus, it is not possible to use the same formula for area that we used in part (a). Of the several ways to approach this problem, the method that many students attempt first usually leads to very difficult algebra and arithmetic. This approach will be illustrated briefly.

First, construct altitude TQ and the area of $\triangle RST = \frac{1}{2}(RS)(TQ)$. The geometric ideas are easy, but actually finding height TQ requires some thought. Without having a formula for finding the distance from a point to a line, it is necessary to find the equations of RS and TQ and then solve the system to find point Q. The length formula can then be used to find TQ, and the area follows. The calculations are arithmetically tedious and will not be presented here. Instead, the method in the next solution will be shown in detail.

Begin by constructing RE and TG perpendicular to the x-axis. This partitions, or subdivides, the figure into one trapezoid and three triangles. Now observe the interesting relationship!

Area of $\triangle RST$ = area of trapezoid $REGT$ + area of $\triangle TGS$ – area of $\triangle RES$.

The area of a trapezoid is $\frac{1}{2}(a+b)d$, where a and b are the lengths of the parallel sides and d is the perpendicular distance between them. To obtain the area of $REGT$ we need vertical lengths $ER = 7$ and $GT = 11$, and horizontal lengths $EG = 6 - 1 = 5$, $GS = 10 - 6 = 4$, and $ES = 10 - 1 = 9$.

The advantage of constructing lines perpendicular to the x-axis is that the required lengths for the sides of the newly created figures come directly from the x and y coordinates of the vertex points. This keeps the arithmetic very simple and allows for a quick solution.

Thus, area $\triangle RST = \frac{1}{2}\left[(ER+GT)(EG)+(GT)(GS)-(ES)(ER)\right]$

$$= \frac{1}{2}\left[(7+11)(5)+(11)(4)-(9)(7)\right]$$

$$= \frac{1}{2}[90+44-63]$$

$$= 35.5.$$

In conclusion, the area of triangle RST is less than the area of triangle AOB by 0.8 square units.

The following list of formulas and special properties make up the tool kit for a beginning student of analytic geometry.

Some Geometric Concepts and Formulas

1. Express the coordinates of a moving, or general, point in the form (x, y).
2. Express the coordinates of fixed points in forms such as (a, b), (x_1, y_1), (x_2, y_2), etc.
3. If any two fixed points are defined by $A(x_1, y_1)$ and $B(x_2, y_2)$, then

    (a) the horizontal directed distance is
    $AQ = x_2 - x_1$

    (b) the vertical directed distance is $QB = y_2 - y_1$

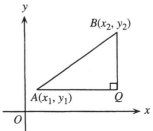

(c)   the distance between points A and B is $AB = \sqrt{(x_2 - x_1)^2 + (y_2 - y_1)^2}$

(d)   the slope of the line AB is $\dfrac{y_2 - y_1}{x_2 - x_1}$

(e)   the midpoint of line segment AB is $\left(\dfrac{x_2 + x_1}{2}, \dfrac{y_2 + y_1}{2}\right)$.

The Formulas for some Geometric Loci

1.   The equation of a straight line with slope m and passing through (x_1, y_1) is $y - y_1 = m(x - x_1)$.
2.   The equation of a straight line with y-intercept b and slope m is $y = mx + b$.
3.   The equation of a circle with centre (a, b) and radius r is $(x - a)^2 + (y - b)^2 = r^2$.
4.   The equation of a circle with centre the origin and radius r is $x^2 + y^2 = r^2$.
5.   The equation of a parabola with vertex at the origin and opening vertically is $y = ax^2$.
6.   The equation of a parabola with vertex at the origin and opening horizontally is $x = ay^2$.

Special Geometric Properties

1.   Suppose two straight lines have slopes m_1 and m_2.

Then,

(a)   if the lines are parallel, $m_1 = m_2$

(b)· if $m_1 = m_2$, the lines are parallel

(c)   if the lines are perpendicular, $m_1 = \dfrac{-1}{m_2}$ or $m_1 m_2 = -1$

(d)   if $m_1 m_2 = -1$, the lines are perpendicular.

2.   If the equation of a straight line is in the form $ax + by + c = 0$, its slope is $-\dfrac{a}{b}$.

3.   If a point $P(a, b)$ is on a locus, the coordinates of the point must satisfy the equation of the locus.

4.   If the coordinates of a point P satisfy the equation of a locus, the point must lie on the locus.

5.   If two loci intersect at one or more points, the points may be found by solving the equations for the two loci.

6.   If two algebraic equations in two variables are solved and produce real solutions, these solutions define the points of intersection between the two loci defined by these equations.

Problems

1. The point $A(-2, y)$ is on the line that passes through the points $T(0, -2)$ and $W(4, 0)$. Find the value of y.

2. Points P, Q, and R divide the line segment from $A(0, 2)$ to $C(6, 0)$ into four equal parts. Find the slope of OR, where O is the origin.

3. Determine the values of t and k so that the lines represented by $tx - 2y + k = 0$ and $3x + y - t = 0$ intersect at $(-2, 1)$.

4. A straight line l passes through the midpoint, M, of the line from $A(-3, 4)$ to $B(7, -2)$.

   (a) Find the equation of the straight line that passes through M and has a slope that is one more than the slope of AB.

   (b) If the point (k, m) is on the line l, express m in terms of k.

5. The line joining $A(2, 6)$ to $B(8, 2)$ is one side of an isosceles triangle. If the x-coordinate of the third vertex, P, is -5, and $AP = BP$, find the y-coordinate of P.

6. (a) The midpoints of adjacent sides of quadrilateral $CART$ are joined to form a new quadrilateral $KMPQ$. If the given points are $A(5, 6)$, $R(10, 2)$, $T(3, -8)$, and $C(-3, -2)$, show that figure $KMPQ$ is a parallelogram.

   (b) Generalize part (a) to any quadrilateral $CART$ and show that the same result occurs when the midpoints are joined.

7. Triangle PQR has vertices $P(3, 4)$, $Q(3, 1)$ and $R(8, 1)$. Find the equation of the bisector of angle PQR.

8. Determine whether the right bisector of the line from $A(2, 5)$ to $B(8, 1)$ passes through the point $T(-8, -17)$.

9. Determine the area of the triangular region enclosed by the lines defined by $4x - 7y + 20 = 0$, $x + y = 6$, and the x-axis.

10. A point W is located on the x-axis so that it is 13 units from the point $R(7, 5)$. Find the coordinates of W.

11. The points A and B are located in the first quadrant, equidistant from the origin O. If the slope of OA is 7 and the slope of OB is 1, find the slope of AB.

12. One side of a $\triangle RAT$ is defined by $R(-2,9)$ and $T(13,6)$. Find the point A if it is located on the x-axis so that angle $A = 90°$.

13. The tunnel under a river has a cross section in the shape of a circular arc. If the arc has a maximum height above the road of 11 metres, and the width of the tunnel at the road level is 36 m, then find (to one decimal place) the radius of the circular cross section.

14. (a) A parabola is defined to be the locus of a point P that moves so that the distance from P to a fixed point (the focus) is equal to the perpendicular distance from P to a fixed line (the directrix). Find the equation of the parabola with focus $F(0,3)$ and directrix $y = -3$. Sketch a graph of the parabola.

    (b) Generalize part (a) by using focus (o, p) and directrix $y = -p$.

15. A particle moving about a circle with radius 10 and centre the origin, is released at the point $R(8, -6)$ and begins to follow a straight line path. Determine if the particle will collide with an object located at the point $Q(100, 120)$.

16. The three towns Alway, Love, Math are located on a coordinate map at $A(-10, 70)$, $L(0, 20)$ and $M(60, 20)$. Determine the location of Who-ville so that W is equidistant from towns A, L, and M.

17. A parallelogram has vertices $P(-3, -1)$, $Q(0, a)$, $R(7, 11)$, and $S(b, c)$.

    (a) Find the value of $a + b + c$.

    (b) If a and c are integers with $6 \le a \le 9$, then find how many different locations are possible for points Q and S.

18. A parabolic tunnel has a height of 6 m at the centre and the base width from wall to wall is also 6 m. Find the maximum width allowed for a 4 m wide truck so that it can just pass through the tunnel if it is driven down the centre of the road.

19. Find the point on the line $3x - 2y + 37 = 0$ that is equally distant from the points $A(2, 7)$ and $B(4, -1)$.

20. A circle with centre $C(2, -3)$ touches the straight line defined by $3x - 4y + 2 = 0$ at the point A. Find the equation of the circle.

21. A locus is traced out by a point P which moves so that the area of triangle PUB is equal to the square of the length of QP, where U is $(-1, 0)$, B is $(1, 0)$ and Q is the foot of the perpendicular from P to the y-axis.

    (a)   Find the equation of this locus.

    (b)   Identify and sketch the locus.

22. (a)   Find the area of $\triangle BAR$ where B is $(-1, 5)$, A is $(11, 2)$ and R is $(5, 8)$.

    (b)   Use points $B(x_1, y_1)$, $A(x_2, y_2)$ and $R(x_3, y_3)$ to generalize the result in part (a).

23. Find the area of the triangle defined by points $A(7, -4)$, $B(-3, -1)$, and $C(4, 5)$.

24. In the diagram P is any point on the circle and AB is a diameter. Prove that angle APB is always a right angle. (We say that $\angle APB$ is subtended by diameter AB).

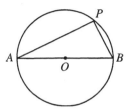

25. The line segment AB, where A is $(2, -4)$ and B is $(10, 8)$, is divided at Q in the ratio 3:5. Find the coordinates of Q.

Chapter 6   Properties of Integers, Divisibility

There is, it seems, an endless supply of problems that require an understanding of the properties of numbers. Included in them are problems that demonstrate amazing facts. Consider the following:

For any two-digit number in which the digits are non-zero and not the same, reverse the digits to obtain a new two-digit number, and take the difference between the two numbers. The difference is always divisible by 9.

You might convince yourself that this is true by trying a number of examples, but you can't be certain unless you try all possible numbers. While you may be willing to do that for two-digit numbers (after all there aren't that many to try), you may be less enthusiastic if asked to repeat the exercise for three-digit numbers. Surely, you say, there must be some way of justifying the statement without having to try them all.

Well, there is (hurrah!), and it depends on a very simple understanding of the construction of numbers. How does one construct the two-digit number 73 when given the digits 7 and 3? The answer, of course, is that we multiply 7 by 10, to give it place value, and add 3. That is, given the digits 7 and 3, we form a two-digit number from $7 \times 10 + 3 = 73$.

If we want to talk about a general two-digit number, we say that the digits are a and b (remembering that the tens digit a cannot be 0 and that we'd better know whether or not b can be 0) and then the two digit number is $a \times 10 + b$ or $10a + b$. If we are sure that b isn't 0, then we can easily form the number with the digits reversed. It is $10b + a$.

Note that the problem posed is now very easy to address. Any two digit number in which the digits are not 0 and are not equal can be represented by $10a + b$. The number formed by reversing the digits is $10b + a$, and the difference between them is $(10a + b) - (10b + a) = 9(a - b)$. Is this always positive? Do we care? Can we be certain that the difference is divisible by 9?

Use the same technique to do the following problem. Solutions to the examples are given at the end of this section.

Example 1
Show that the difference between any three-digit number, in which no digits are 0 or equal, and the number formed by reversing the digits is always a multiple of 99.

The fact that every number can be written in the form $1000a + 100b + 10c + d$, if it has four digits, and that the same pattern applies for numbers with any number of digits, is extremely useful.

Now try this one, which involves numbers in a base different than 10.

Example 2
The number 26 (base p) multiplied by 3, gives 75 (base p). What is the base p?

A second property that helps in the examination of the structure of integers is the fact that any integer can be factored so that it is the product of prime factors.

For example, $42 = 2 \times 3 \times 7$ and $72 = 2 \times 2 \times 2 \times 3 \times 3$ or $2^3 \times 3^2$.

In fact, every integer can be written in the form

$$N = 2^a 3^b 5^c 7^d \cdots$$

where every prime number appears *if needed* and where the exponents indicate the number of times each prime occurs.

Example 3

Write 38 250 as the product of primes.

Is there a property that allows for the identification of integers as perfect squares? Let us examine a listing of the first few perfect squares greater than 1:

$$4 = 2^2$$
$$9 = 3^2$$
$$16 = 4^2 = 2^4$$
$$25 = 5^2$$
$$36 = 6^2 = 2^2 \times 3^2$$
$$49 = 7^2$$
$$64 = 8^2 = 2^6$$
$$81 = 9^2 = 3^4$$
$$100 = 10^2 = 2^2 \times 5^2$$
$$121 = 11^2$$
$$144 = 12^2 = 2^4 \times 3^2$$

In every perfect square any prime that occurs in the number's prime factorization does so an even number of times.

Example 4

Is the number $N = 3192 \times 179\,550$ a perfect square?

(You can certainly do this with a calculator, but in order to appreciate the property, do it by factoring the numbers).

Factoring large integers is a difficult task, but is made much easier if you know how to determine when divisibility by common integers occurs. Here's a list of divisibility rules.

An integer N is divisible by
- 2 if it is even
- 3 if the sum of the digits of N is divisible by 3
- 4 if the last two digits of N form a two digit number that is divisible by 4
- 5 if the last digit is 0 or 5
- 6 if N is divisible by both 2 and 3
- 8 if the last three digits of N form a three digit number that is divisible by 8
- 9 if the sum of the digits of N is divisible by 9
- 11 if the sum of the odd-numbered digits (1st, 3rd, etc.) minus the sum of the even-numbered digits (2nd, 4th, etc.) is divisible by 11
- any composite number if it is divisible by each of the prime factors of the composite number.

We aren't going to prove these, but it is a good idea for you to take a few minutes with your calculator and some numbers - you can easily make them up - and satisfy yourself that the rules work. For example, 17 093 824 is divisible by 8 and by 11, and therefore by 88.

This prime factorization idea is also a useful means of determining how many divisors an integer has. (Isn't it remarkable how a simple idea can be so useful?) Consider the question "How many divisors does the number 252 have?"

By trial and error, we could determine the answer, but now that we know about the value of determining the prime factors of a number, that seems like a sensible approach.

$$252 - 4 \times 63$$
$$= 4 \times 9 \times 7$$
$$= 2^2 \times 3^2 \times 7$$

Clearly, 252 is divisible by 2, 4, 3, 9, 7, and also by 6, 12, 18, 36, 14, 28, 21, 63, 42, 126, 84, as well as by 1 and 252. You can, and should, check them all. There are eighteen divisors.

The question we pose is whether it is possible to determine how many divisors 252 has without actually finding them all, and we return to the prime factorization process for the answer. Note that $252 = 2^2 \times 3^2 \times 7$. Hence, any divisor of 252 must be some combination of 2, 3, and 7. If we say that *any* divisor is of the form $2^a 3^b 7^c$, then by allowing a to be 0, 1, or 2, b to be 0, 1, or 2, and c to be 0 or 1, we can create any divisor of 252. For $(a, b, c) = (0, 0, 0)$ we obtain the divisor 1; for $(a, b, c) = (1, 0, 0)$ we obtain the divisor 2; for $(a, b, c) = (1, 2, 1)$ we obtain the divisor 126; and so on.

The question now becomes "How many (a, b, c) triples are there?" There are three possible values for a and also for b, and there are two possible values for c, so there are $3 \times 3 \times 2 = 18$ (a, b, c) triples and therefore 18 divisors.

Example 5
How many divisors, other than 1 and the number itself, does 23 400 have?

Divisibility properties are useful in problems involving consecutive positive integers. If we consider any two consecutive integers, one must be even and hence divisible by 2. This reasoning goes a long way, and by thinking about it (and trying a few examples) you can quickly convince yourself that in three consecutive integers there must be one that is divisible by 2 and one (maybe the same one!) that is divisible by 3. In four consecutive integers there must be one divisible by 2, one divisible by 3, and one divisible by 4. In fact, in k consecutive integers there must be one divisible by k, one by $(k-1)$, one by $(k-2)$, etc., all the way to one divisible by 2. In other words, the product of k consecutive positive integers is divisible by $k!$, where $k! = k \times (k-1) \times (k-2) \times \cdots \times 2 \times 1$.

The amazing thing is that this statement is also true for the product of k consecutive positive *even* integers. Now you speculate on what will happen if you meet a problem involving the product of k consecutive odd integers.

Example 6
Prove that for m a positive integer, the expression $m^3 + 3m^2 + 2m$ is divisible by 6 for all values of m.

SOLUTIONS TO EXAMPLES

Example 1
If the digits are a, b, and c, a three-digit number can be represented by $100a + 10b + c$, with $1 \le a, b, c \le 9$.

The number with the digits reversed is $100c + 10b + a$.

The difference is $(100a + 10b + c) - (100c + 10b + a) = 99a - 99c$
$$= 99(a - c).$$

This number, whether positive or negative, is always divisible by 99.

Example 2
The number 26 (base p) can be represented by $2p + 6$.

The number 75 (base p) can be represented by $7p + 5$.

Then $\quad 3(2p + 6) = 7p + 5$
$$6p + 18 = 7p + 5$$
$$p = 13.$$

The base p is 13.

Example 3
$$38250 = 10 \times 3825$$
$$= 2 \times 5 \times 5 \times 765$$
$$= 2 \times 5 \times 5 \times 5 \times 153$$
$$= 2 \times 5^3 \times 9 \times 17$$
$$= 2 \times 3^2 \times 5^3 \times 17.$$

Example 4

$$N = 3192 \times 179\,550$$

$$= 6 \times 532 \times 10 \times 17\,955 \qquad \text{(Start by finding any factors you can)}$$

$$= 2 \times 3 \times 2 \times 266 \times 2 \times 5 \times 5 \times 3591$$

$$= 2^4 \times 3 \times 133 \times 5^2 \times 3 \times 1197$$

$$= 2^4 \times 3^2 \times 5^2 \times 133 \times 9 \times 133$$

$$= 2^4 \times 3^2 \times 5^2 \times 7^2 \times 19^2 \qquad \text{(Since } 133 = 7 \times 19)$$

$$= \left(2^2 \times 3^2 \times 5 \times 7 \times 19\right)^2.$$

Hence N is a perfect square.

Example 5

$$23\,400 = 234 \times 100$$

$$= 2 \times 117 \times 2^2 \times 5^2$$

$$= 2^3 \times 5^2 \times 3^2 \times 13$$

$$= 2^3 \times 3^2 \times 5^2 \times 13.$$

The number of divisors, including 1 and $23\,400$ itself, is $4 \times 3 \times 3 \times 2 = 72$.
The number of divisors, excluding 1 and $23\,400$, is 70.

Example 6

$$N = m^3 + 3m^2 + 2m = m\left(m^2 + 3m + 2\right)$$

$$= m(m+1)(m+2).$$

If m is a positive integer then m, $m+1$ and $m+2$ are consecutive integers.
Hence one of these is divisible by 2 and one is divisible by 3.
Therefore N is divisible by at least 6.

We note that N is, for some values of m, divisible by integers larger than 6. If, for example, m is even, then $m+2$ is also even, and one of these factors is divisible by 4. Given that one of the three integers (we don't know which) is divisible by 3, we have N divisible by at least 24. This is not always true, of course, as you can see by trying a few possible triples. We limit ourselves to the minimal statement that we can show is always true.

FACTS TO KEEP AT FINGER TIP

* we can represent integers by using $10a + b$ (or variations thereon)
* every integer can be expressed as the product of primes
* there are a number of relatively simple divisibility rules
* the number of divisors of an integer can be determined from the prime factorization of the integer
* consecutive integers contain some very nice divisibility properties.

Here we are! You are ready to tackle some problems. Remember to make use of known properties - and don't be afraid to doodle. We often determine the key to a problem by simply trying a few things.

Problems

1. How many perfect squares greater than 1 divide 4000 exactly?

2. Determine all numbers n between 10 and 200 where n is a prime and $n - 1$ is a perfect square.

3. Using only the digits 0 and 1, four-digit numeric codes (such as 0110) are created. How many such codes are there in which zeros are never adjacent?

4. In the "Big 15" Lottery, tickets are printed and numbered from 1000 to 9999 inclusive, one number to a ticket. A number is a winner if its hundreds digit is 8, its tens digit is 6, and it is divisible by 15. How many winning tickets are there?

5. Each of the numbers 2, 5, 11, and 13 is assigned in some order to p, q, r, and s. What is the largest possible value of $3pq + 2qr + qs$?

6. How many positive three-digit integers are there such that the sum of the three digits is 24?

7. When 54 is subtracted from a two-digit number, the result is a number having the same two digits reversed in order. Determine all two-digit numbers satisfying this property.

8. Forty cards are numbered consecutively from 1 to 40. The cards are shuffled and sorted into four piles with ten cards in each. If the sum of the ten cards in any pile is determined, how many different sums could possibly be obtained?

9. (a) If 630 is the product of three positive integers whose sum is 38, what are the three integers?

    (b) If 630 is expressed as the product of three positive integers, what integers could be used so that their sum is (i) the largest possible, (ii) the smallest possible?

10. The five-digit number $9T67U$, where T and U are digits, is divisible by 36. Determine all possible values for T and U.

11. It is required to determine a value for T such that the five-digit number $N = 6813T$ is divisible by 66. Is this possible?

12. How many two-digit integers are increased by 11 when the order of the digits is reversed?

13. (a) What is the number of ten-digit positive integers, consisting only of ones and zeros, with the first digit always one, that are divisible by 9?

   (b) Repeat part (a) for eleven-digit positive integers.

14. Every positive three-digit number is written on a separate card. All of these cards are placed in a box. Mary selects cards at random and calculates the sum of the three digits on each card. How many cards must she select to be certain of having two cards whose sums are the same?

15. If p is a prime number greater than 5, determine the sum of all possible divisors of $15p$.

16. Three prime numbers a, b, and c are such that $a + b = c$ and $a < b < c < 40$. Determine all possible sets $\{a, b, c\}$.

17. Determine the smallest integer that is a perfect square, is greater than 20 000, and is divisible by 392.

18. If the repeating decimal represented by $0.a7a7a7\ldots$, where a is a single digit, is expressed as a fraction in reduced form, what value of a gives the fraction with the smallest sum of its numerator and denominator?

19. Given that m is an even positive integer, prove that $m^3 - 4m$ is always divisible by 48.

20. The number 27 572 is a palindrome because it reads the same backwards and forwards. Determine the largest possible five-digit palindrome in each of the following cases:

   (a) the number is divisible by 6

   (b) the number is divisible by 12

21. Let a and b be two positive integers, where $a > b$. Find all pairs a, b such that the sum of their sum, their positive difference, their product, and their quotient is 36.

22. (a) Two consecutive odd positive integers have the property that the smaller number is divisible by 5 and the larger number is divisible by 7. Determine the smallest pair of numbers greater than 20 that satisfy this requirement.

   (b) Can you state general expressions for the numbers from which you could determine other pairs with the same property?

23. Fractions of the form $\frac{a}{b}$ are created such that a and b are positive integers and $a + b = 333$. How many such fractions are less than one and cannot be reduced? (That is, the numerator and denominator have no common factor).

24. Determine all ordered pairs of integers (x, y) that satisfy the equation $x^2 + 6x + y^2 = 4$.

25. The sets $\{1\}, \{3, 5\}, \{7, 9, 11\}, \cdots$ consist of positive odd integers in order from smallest to largest. Each set contains one more element than the preceding set. The first element in each set after the first is two more than the last element in the preceding set.

    (a)   What is the sum of the elements in the 21st set?

    (b)   What is the sum of the elements in the nth set?

26. Determine the remainder if 1995^{1993} is divided by 100.

27. If 49 in base p and 94 in base q represent the same number in base 10, what is the least possible value for the number?

28. A two-digit number has the property that if it is multiplied by 888 it gives the same product as the number obtained by reversing the two digits and then multiplying by 1752. What is the number?

29. How many different six-digit numbers can be formed by arranging the digits 2, 3, 7, 7, 8, 8?

30. The product of five odd prime numbers is a five-digit number of the form $strst$, where $r = 0$. How many such numbers are possible?

Chapter 7   Miscellaneous Problems

The chapters preceding this one have each dealt with problems drawn from two or three general areas. When you solved problems in these chapters you had numerous examples to help you get started. This is not the case in chapter 7 because the problems come from a wide variety of sources. Now you have a chance to flex the problem solving muscles you have been developing, for here you must decide what area or areas of mathematics may be useful in attacking the problem.

This may seem daunting, but it shouldn't be. The initial steps are the same as before:
(i)   read and understand the problem
(ii)   review in your mind any mathematical properties pertaining to the information given to you in the problems   .
(iii) make sure you are clear in your mind just what you are required to do in the problem.

Once you understand the problem and have thought a bit about the given information, you must do something. Usually problems don't solve themselves; they need our help. To help them, we need to try something and see if it works. If it doesn't, we must be prepared to start again, or back track.

With practice, we begin to recognize when a particular approach is not leading us to a solution. To develop this sense, we need to follow many blind leads. The following example may help to illustrate some of these comments.

Example 1
In the chart, the products of the numbers represented by the letters in each of the rows and columns are given. For example, $xy = 6$ and $xz = 12$. If x, y, z, and w are integers, what is the value of xw?

x	y	6
z	w	50
12	25	

Discussion
Paraphrasing the question, we're given $xy = 6$, $xz = 12$, $zw = 50$, and $yw = 25$, and need to find xw. The problem also says that x, y, z, and w are integers. This together with the fact that the given products are all positive says that x, y, z, and w are either all positive or all negative. Without loss of generality we will assume that they are non-negative. We also note that none of x, y, z, or w is zero (why?).

Now, by just playing around with the possible values of x, y, z, and w we can probably fill in the chart fairly quickly and obtain

6	1	6
2	25	50
12	25	

From this we get $xw = 6 \times 25 = 150$.

But is this the only answer? Let's try to find out.

Since $xy = 6$ and $yw = 25$, then $xy^2w = 150$.

Since $xz = 12$ and $zw = 50$, then $xz^2w = 600$.

Hence $\dfrac{xy^2w}{xz^2w} = \dfrac{150}{600}$

$$\dfrac{y^2}{z^2} = \dfrac{1}{4}$$

$$z^2 = 4y^2$$

$$z = 2y. \quad \text{(Why is } z \text{ not equal to } -2y\text{?)}$$

Now go back to $xy = 6$. The possible values of (x, y) are $(6, 1), (1, 6), (3, 2)$, and $(2, 3)$. That is, the possible values of y are 1, 6, 2, and 3.

From $z = 2y$, the possible values of z are 2, 12, 4, and 6.

But $z = 12$ gives $12w = 50$ and there is no integer value of w that satisfies this. Similarly $z = 4$ and $z = 6$ are impossible.

Thus the only possible value of xw is 150.

Here is a second approach which may prove to be easier.

We are given $xy = 6$, $wy = 25$, $zx = 12$ and $zw = 50$.

By addition we get $xy + zx = 6 + 12$

$$x(y + z) = 18 \qquad (1)$$

also $\qquad wy + wz = 25 + 50$

$$x(y + z) = 75 \qquad (2)$$

Since x, y, z, and w are integers we know that $(y + z)$ is a factor of both 18 and 75, and the only common factors of 18 and 75 are 1 and 3, so $y + z = 1$ or $y + z = 3$. $y + z = 1$ is not possible since x, y, z, and w are all positive integers.

Thus $y + z = 3$ which gives $x = 6$, $w = 25$, and so $xw = 150$.

The point in doing the second solution is to further illustrate that one's first idea, while perhaps very good, will often be only one of several approaches which will lead to a solution. In fact, first ideas often lead to dead ends.

The importance of trying to look at a problem from different approaches cannot be stressed too much. There is a lot to be gained by looking for alternate solutions.

Let's consider another example:

Example 2

Given that $21xy^2$ and $15xy$ are perfect squares, where x and y are positive integers, determine the minimum value of $x + y$.

Discussion

We are given that x and y are positive integers, and that $21xy^2$ and $15xy$ are perfect squares. What does this last point tell us? Since they are perfect squares their square roots are positive integers, and, more importantly, their prime factors must all appear an even number of times. For example, if 2 is a factor of a perfect square then 2^2 must also be a factor.

We begin by writing $21xy^2 = 3 \cdot 7 \cdot x \cdot y^2$.

Since y^2 is already a perfect square, the smallest possible value of x is $3.7 = 21$. This ensures that prime factors occur in pairs.

Now look at $15xy$.

$$15xy = 3 \cdot 5 \cdot x \cdot y$$
$$= 3 \cdot 5 \cdot 3.7y \quad (\text{using } x = 21)$$
$$= 3^2 \cdot 5 \cdot 7 \cdot y.$$

The smallest possible value of y is $5.7 = 35$.
Hence $x + y = 21 + 35 = 56$.

The most important thing to keep in mind as you try the problems is that many basic strategies still work. Don't just look for a "formula" to use. Allow your mind to explore different avenues of attack and don't become discouraged if you don't succeed the first time.

In the questions that follow, similar problems have not necessarily been grouped together and there will be many that don't fit within topics you have studied in the past.

Problems

1. In the diagram, each of the seven circles is coloured so that no two circles connected by a line segment have the same colour. What is the minimum number of different colours required?

2. Starting with 2, Barbie lists every positive integer which is not a perfect square. What is the 100th number on Barbie's list?

3. In the diagram, all edges have length 1. Determine the length of the longest path from Q to S, which doesn't go along any edge more than once.

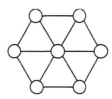
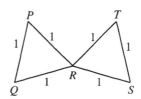

4. Five integers have an average of 69. The middle integer (the median) is 83. The most frequently occurring integer (the mode) is 85. The range of the five integers is 70. What is the second smallest of the five integers?

5. The lengths of the side of an equilateral triangle are given by $7a - 3$, $5a + 15$ and $4x$. Determine all possible values for x.

6. The eight digits 6, 5, 5, 4, 4, 3, 2, and 1 are used to form two three-digit numbers and one two-digit number. Determine the largest possible sum of these numbers.

7. In a magic square, the sums of the entries in each row, in each column, and in each diagonal are all equal. In the magic square shown, determine the value of N.

15	1	11
		N
	17	

8. In the diagram, all the angles are right angles and the indicated lengths are equal. Determine the number of squares of all sizes in the diagram.

9. A league has 10 teams, and each team plays each of the other teams exactly twice. What is the total number of games played?

10. A positive number is placed in each of the small squares in the diagram. The products of the three numbers in any row, any column, or any diagonal are equal. Find a relation between x and y.

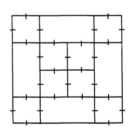

		2
4		x
y	1	

11. Each of three senior citizens was born on February 21. Their ages, in years, on February 22, 1995 were three consecutive primes whose sum was 235. In what year was the oldest of the three born?

12. Each of the integers from 1 to 9 is placed, one per
    circle, into the pattern shown. The sums along each
    of the four sides are equal. What integers could be
    placed in the middle circle?

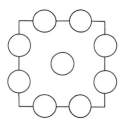

13. An integer is chosen randomly from the integers 1 to 101 inclusive. What is the probability
    that at least one of the digits of the integer chosen is a 7?

14. Bo Jest and his troops fill their canteens at
    oasis A in the desert and must march on
    foot to a second oasis, B. The first oasis is
    48 km north of a straight freshwater canal.
    The second oasis is 36 km north of the
    canal and 120 km east of the first oasis.
    The troops march at 4 km/h but must
    replenish their water supply at least every
    15 hours. Bo knows mathematics and he
    calculates the shortest time for the march.
    How long will the march take?

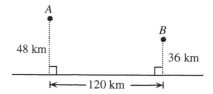

15. If $4 \le x \le 12$, and $6 \le y \le 10$, and $S = x - y$, what is the largest possible interval for S?

16. An *ascending* integer occurs when each digit is greater than any digit which preceeds it.
    An example is 478. How many ascending integers occur between 200 and 300?

17. Given $\frac{1}{a} + \frac{1}{b} = \frac{7}{2}$, and $\frac{1}{a} - \frac{1}{b} = -\frac{5}{2}$, determine the value of $a + b$.

18. A gardener has a push mower and a riding mower. It takes her five hours to cut the entire
    lawn with the push mower but only 70 minutes with the riding mower. After 90% of the lawn
    was cut using the riding mower, the remainder was cut using the push mower. How many
    minutes did it take to cut the lawn?

19. The numbers 1, 2, 3, 4, and 5 are to be placed in the
    grid in such a way that each occurs only once in
    any row, column, or diagonal. Find the values of P
    and Q.

1				
	2		5	
		3	Q	1
2				3
P	3		1	

20. Of 45 students in a mathematics class, 27 own a bicycle and 22 own a skateboard. Three students do not own either one. How many students own both a bicycle and a skateboard?

21. A painted $10 \times 8 \times 4$ block is cut into $1 \times 1 \times 1$ cubes. How many of the $1 \times 1 \times 1$ cubes do not have any painted surfaces?

22. Bart squeezes out a complete tube of toothpaste to make a continuous line of toothpaste, 10 m in length, down the centre of the sidewalk. If the diameter of the circular opening of the tube had been half as large, how long would the line of toothpaste have been?

23. When the base of a triangle is increased by 10%, by what percentage must the altitude be decreased to keep the area unchanged?

24. The diagram shows a system of three gears. Gear A has 20 teeth, gear B has 40 teeth, and gear C has 10 teeth. If gear A rotates clockwise at 10 rpm (revolutions per minute), describe how gear C will rotate.

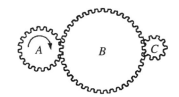

25. The scales in the diagram are balanced. Determine the number of Y's required to balance one Z.

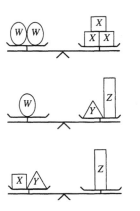

26. Two cyclists start from the same place at 1:15 p.m. One travels north at 24 km/h and the other travels east at 32 km/h. When will they be 130 km apart?

27. Given $xy = \dfrac{x}{y} = x - y$, where $y \neq 0$, determine the value of $x + y$.

28. A length of rope is cut into two pieces at a randomly selected point. What is the probability that the longer piece is at least twice as long as the shorter piece?

29. The Ancients built square-based structures similar to those shown in the diagram. They began with 1000 identical cubes and wished to build as many structures as possible. The first structure contained two layers. Beside it was constructed a second structure with three layers. This process was continued as shown until the number of cubes left was not sufficient to build the next structure. How many cubes were left?

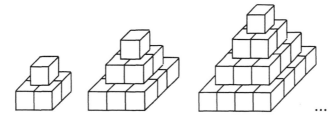

30. On planet Binad, a Bank Cash machine uses eight ON-OFF switches numbered 1 to 8 to allow deposits to and withdrawals from an account. All the switches start out OFF. When switch n is flipped ON, the balance of the account changes by $(-1)^n(2)^n$ dollars. For example, if switches 4 and 7 are flipped ON and the others left OFF, a withdrawal of 112 dollars is made. How many switches must be turned ON to deposit 114 dollars?

31. A wrapping machine runs five days a week at a constant rate. On Monday, it wrapped 60 parcels and 70 catalogs. On Tuesday, it wrapped 80 parcels and 40 catalogs. On Wednesday, Thursday, and Friday, it wrapped only catalogs. How many catalogs were wrapped during the week?

32. A five-digit number is created, using each of the digits 1, 3, 5, 7, and 9 once. Each of the digits in the tens and thousands positions is larger than its neighbouring digits. How many such five-digit numbers can be formed?

33. Given $A = \{1, 2, 3, 5, 8, 13, 21, 34, 55\}$, how many of the numbers between 3 and 89 cannot be written as the sum of two elements of the set?

Chapter 8   Challenge Problems

Our purpose in this chapter is to give you some exposure to problems that are interesting and non-routine. Problems have been selected that are neither technically difficult nor which place unusual demands on students. Rather, we have chosen problems which require some creativity or unusual thought for their solution.

When students first encounter problems of this type, they often become discouraged or disinterested. What they fail to realize is that all problem solvers start from the same point. What is needed for success is perseverance and hard work. Take your time and try and think about the problem without immediately referring to the answer. Give yourself some time to allow your creativity to flow. The effort is worth the result.

In this chapter, we will provide you with some worked examples along with a tool kit of results and ideas to help you in solving the problems. Enjoy yourself and work hard.

Concept 1   Factoring the Sum and Difference of Cubes

$$x^3 + y^3 = (x + y)(x^2 - xy + y^2)$$
$$x^3 - y^3 = (x - y)(x^2 + xy + y^2)$$

Notice that the sum of cubes can be rewritten in the following way:

$$x^3 + y^3 = (x + y)(x^2 - xy + y^2)$$
$$= (x + y)\left[(x + y)^2 - 2xy - xy\right]$$
$$= (x + y)\left[(x + y)^2 - 3xy\right].$$

Example 1

Given the equations $x + y = 30$ and $x^3 + y^3 = 8100$, determine the value of $x^2 + y^2$.

Solution

We know that $x^2 + y^2 = (x + y)^2 - 2xy$ and, since $x + y = 30$, it is only necessary to calculate xy.

From above, $x^3 + y^3 = (x + y)\left[(x + y)^2 - 3xy\right]$.

Now by substituting $x^3 + y^3 = 8100$ and $x + y = 30$, we find, $8100 = 30(30^2 - 3xy)$

$$270 = 900 - 3xy$$
$$xy = 210.$$

Therefore $x^2 + y^2 = 30^2 - 2(210)$
$$= 480.$$

Concept 2   Telescoping Series

Show that $\dfrac{1}{n(n+1)} = \dfrac{1}{n} - \dfrac{1}{n+1}$.

This can be shown to be true by writing $\dfrac{1}{n(n+1)} = \dfrac{A}{n} + \dfrac{B}{n+1}$

$$= \dfrac{(A+B)n+A}{n(n+1)}.$$

By comparing the numerators on the left and right sides, $A = 1$ and $A + B = 0$, and so $B = -1$.

Therefore $\dfrac{1}{n(n+1)} = \dfrac{1}{n} - \dfrac{1}{n+1}$.

Example 2

Determine the sum: $\dfrac{25}{72} + \dfrac{25}{90} + \dfrac{25}{110} + \cdots + \dfrac{25}{9900}$.

Solution

If we factor the denominators we notice that $72 = 8 \times 9$, $90 = 9 \times 10$, $110 = 10 \times 11$, ..., $9900 = 99 \times 100$.

Removing 25 as a common factor makes the calculations a little easier.

We then write the series as $25\left(\dfrac{1}{8\times 9} + \dfrac{1}{9\times 10} + \dfrac{1}{10\times 11} + \cdots + \dfrac{1}{99\times 100}\right)$.

Using concept 2, our series can now be rewritten as

$$25\left[\left(\tfrac{1}{8} - \tfrac{1}{9}\right) + \left(\tfrac{1}{9} - \tfrac{1}{10}\right) + \cdots + \left(\tfrac{1}{98} - \tfrac{1}{99}\right) + \left(\tfrac{1}{99} - \tfrac{1}{100}\right)\right]$$

$$= 25\left[\tfrac{1}{8} + \left(-\tfrac{1}{9} + \tfrac{1}{9}\right) + \left(-\tfrac{1}{10} + \tfrac{1}{10}\right) + \cdots + \left(-\tfrac{1}{99} + \tfrac{1}{99}\right) - \tfrac{1}{100}\right]$$

$$= 25\left(\tfrac{1}{8} - \tfrac{1}{100}\right)$$

$$= 2\tfrac{7}{8} \quad \text{or} \quad 2.875.$$

The required sum is $2\tfrac{7}{8}$ or 2.875.

Concept 3   Areas and Proportions

If two triangles have equal heights, their areas are proportional to the lengths of their bases.

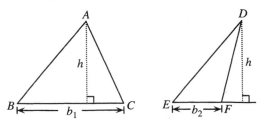

The area of $\triangle ABC = \tfrac{1}{2}b_1 h$ and the area of $\triangle DEF = \tfrac{1}{2}b_2 h$.

Therefore $\dfrac{\text{area of } \triangle ABC}{\text{area of } \triangle DEF} = \dfrac{\frac{1}{2}b_1h}{\frac{1}{2}b_2h}$

$$= \dfrac{b_1}{b_2}.$$

It is also true that if two triangles have equal bases then their areas are proportional to their heights.

Example 3

A triangle ABC is such that F divides AC in the ratio
1:3. The point E divides CB in a 2:1 ratio and D is the
midpoint of AB. Determine what fraction the area of
$\triangle DEF$ is of the area of $\triangle ABC$.

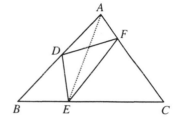

Solution

Join A to E and C to D and mark ratios on the diagram as
shown.
Consider $\triangle AEB$ and its smaller triangles, ADE and BDE.

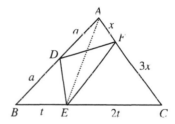

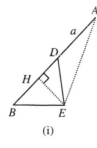 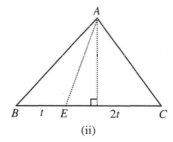

(i)   (ii)

Since $\triangle ADE$ and $\triangle BDE$ have equal bases and equal heights, as shown in diagram (i), they have
the same area.

Using the same reasoning, the area of $\triangle ABE = \frac{1}{3}\triangle ABC$ as shown in diagram (ii).

Since $2\triangle BDE = \triangle ABE$, we have $2\triangle BDE = \frac{1}{3}\triangle ABC$ or $\triangle BDE = \frac{1}{6}\triangle ABC$.

Similarly, we find that $\triangle EFC = \frac{3}{4}\times\frac{2}{3}\triangle ABC$

$$= \frac{1}{2}\triangle ABC$$

and
$$\Delta ADF = \frac{1}{4} \times \frac{1}{2} \Delta ABC$$

$$= \frac{1}{8} \Delta ABC.$$

From this, $\Delta DEF = \Delta ABC - \frac{1}{8}\Delta ABC - \frac{1}{2}\Delta ABC - \frac{1}{6}\Delta ABC$

$$= \frac{24}{24}\Delta ABC - \frac{3}{24}\Delta ABC - \frac{12}{24}\Delta ABC - \frac{4}{24}\Delta ABC$$

$$= \frac{5}{24}\Delta ABC.$$

Thus $\Delta DEF = \frac{5}{24}\Delta ABC.$

Concept 4   Divisors of an Integer

We will illustrate this idea with a single example. Suppose we are trying to find the number of divisors of 675. Writing 675 in factored form, $675 = 3^3 \times 5^2$. If we write the divisors of 3^3 and 5^2 separately and put them in column form we would have:

Divisors of 3^3	Divisors of 5^2
1	1
3	5
3^2	5^2
3^3	

For each of the four divisors in the first column we would have three divisors in the second column, thus making us a total of twelve.

In general, if we write a number in prime factored form as $a^x b^y c^z \ldots$, it will have $(x+1)(y+1)(z+1)\ldots$ divisors which include 1 and the number itself.

Example 4

When 1216 is multiplied by k, where k is a positive integer, the resulting product has exactly 61 different divisors not including one and the product itself. Find k.

Solution

If we assume that the product $1216k$ has 63 factors, instead of 61, the problem is easier because this means we include 1 and $1216k$ as divisors which is the normal procedure when counting divisors.

Factoring is always a good first step when solving problems of this type.

Thus, $1216k = 8 \times 152 \times k$

$$= 8 \times 8 \times 19 \times k$$

$$= 2^6 \times 19 \times k.$$

Also, we know that $63 = 7 \times 3 \times 3$

$$= (6+1)(2+1)(2+1).$$

We are now looking for the smallest value of k which produces the 63 divisors.

After a bit of experimentation we find $1216k = \left(2^6\right)(19)\left(19 \times 3^2\right)$

$$= \left(2^6\right)\left(19^2\right)\left(3^2\right).$$

Therefore $9 \times 19 = 171$ is the smallest value of k.

Additional concepts are provided that are helpful in solving the problems that follow.

1. *Ratios of Sides of Triangles*
   (i)   *The $30° - 60° - 90°$ triangle.*

The sides of a $30° - 60° - 90°$ triangle are in

the ratio $x : x\sqrt{3} : 2x$.

The largest side is opposite the largest angle
and it follows that the smallest side is opposite
the smallest angle.

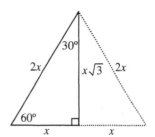

   (i)   *The $45° - 45° - 90°$ triangle.*

The sides of a $45° - 45° - 90°$ triangle are in

the ratio $x : x : x\sqrt{2}$.

2. *Circle Theorems*
   (i)   *Every angle in a semi-circle equals $90°$.*

If AB is a diameter, $\angle C = \angle D = \angle E = 90°$.

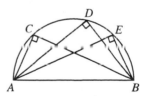

   (ii) *Any right bisector of a chord passes through the
         centre of the circle.*

The right bisectors of chords AB and CD pass
through O.

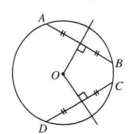

Notice that if a line is drawn from the centre of a circle to the midpoint of a chord, this line is
perpendicular to the chord.

3. *Lowest Common Multiple and Greatest Common Divisor*
The lowest common multiple (l.c.m.) of a set of integers is the smallest integer into which each
element of that set divides evenly.

The greatest common divisor (g.c.d.) of a set of integers is the largest integer that will divide evenly into each element of the given set.

In calculating the l.c.m. or g.c.d., it is best to write them in prime factored form.

Example 5
Find the l.c.m. and g.c.d. of 56 and 80.

Solution

$$56 = 2^3 \times 7$$
$$80 = 2^4 \times 5$$

The l.c.m. of 56 and 80 is $2^4 \times 5 \times 7$ or 560.

The g.c.d. of 56 and 80 is 2^3 or 8.

Notes
1. If two or more integers have a g.c.d. of 1, we say these two numbers are relatively prime. For two such numbers, we would write $(a, b) = 1$. For example, $(8, 15) = 1$.

2. In general, for any set of integers, $\{a, b, c, ...\}$, it is true that
$$\text{l.c.m.} \{a, b, c, ...\} \times \text{g.c.d.} \{a, b, c, ...\} = a \times b \times c \times ....$$

4. Fermat's Principle
If we wish to find a point X on PQ such that the length $AX + BX$ is of minimal length, think of PQ as a mirror and reflect A in PQ to find A'. Join A' to B. The point X is where the line $A'B$ intersects M and will produce the minimal required length.
Note that in producing this minimal length, $\angle AXQ = \angle BXP$.

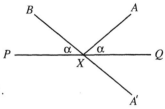

Fermat's Principle states that if a light source is at A and a beam from A bounces off the mirror to B, its path will be of minimal length.

5. Solution of a Quadratic Equation

For any quadratic equation, $ax^2 + bx + c = 0$, its roots are $x = \dfrac{-b \pm \sqrt{b^2 - 4ac}}{2a}$.

Problems

1. Starting from opposite ends of a straight track at the same time, two runners begin jogging at constant rates. Each person runs to the far end of the track and back to his starting position. Their first meeting is 600 m from one end and their second meeting is 300 m from the other end. Find the length of the track, in metres.

2. Two ships, one 200 metres in length and the other 100 metres in length, travel at constant but different speeds. When travelling in opposite directions, it takes 10 seconds for them to completely pass each other. When travelling in the same direction, it takes 25 seconds for them to completely pass each other. Find the speed of the faster ship, in metres per second.

3. A Wizard's assistant is paid in an unusual way. The assistant's paycheque for the first week is one dollar. At the end of each week after the first week, the assistant is paid the amount of money earned the previous week plus two dollars for each week worked so far. Find the amount of the paycheque, in dollars, for the fifty-second week.

4. In the series $S_n = 5.5 + 5.55 + 5.555 + ...$, the nth term has one five before the decimal point and n fives after it. For example, the sixth term is 5.555555.

    (a) Show that $550 < S_{100} < 560$.

    (b) Show that $S_{100} < 556$.

5. A sequence consists of ten terms, all of which are positive integers. The first term is p and the second is q, with $q > p$. Each term thereafter is the sum of the two terms immediately preceding it, and the seventh term is 181. Given that there are exactly two such sequences, show that the ten terms in each sequence have the same sum, and determine this sum.

6. In a square array with 10 rows and 10 columns, the number in the mth row and nth column is given by the product $(2m-1)(3n-1)$. Find the sum of all the elements in the array.

7. The first term in a sequence of numbers is $t_1 = 5$. Succeeding terms are defined by the statement $t_n - t_{n-1} = 2n + 3$ for $n \geq 2$. Find the value of t_{50}.

8. The sum of 28 consecutive odd, positive integers is a perfect cube. Find the smallest integer in this set.

9. Assume the circumference of the earth at the equator is 36 000 km. A satellite is orbiting the earth's centre so that it is always 600 km above a specific point on the equator. Find the speed of the satellite in kilometres per hour.

10. There are exactly k perfect squares which are divisors of 1996^{1996}. Find k.

11. If $f(x) = px + q$ and $f(f(f(x))) = 8x + 21$, where p and q are real numbers, find $p + q$.

12. An ice cube tray has three sections P, Q, and R. Each section measures $4\,cm \times 4\,cm \times 4\,cm$ as shown in the diagram. Section P is full of water, section Q is half full and section R is empty. If the tray is then tipped at an angle of $30°$ to the horizontal, as shown, how much water will end up in section R?

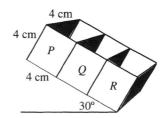

13. Five tiles are arranged in a pattern as shown, with four regular octagons around the square tile. If the central tile has an area of one square unit, find the area covered by the five tiles.

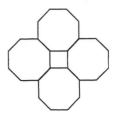

14. At one time, the number of employees in a company was a perfect square. Later, with an increase of 100 employees, the number of employees was one more than a perfect square. Now with an additional increase of 100 employees, the total number is again a perfect square. Find the original number of employees.

15. A cube measuring $10 \times 10 \times 10$ has two mutually perpendicular square holes of the same size cut out. If one-half of the volume of the original cube is removed in this process, find the length of PQ to the nearest tenth.

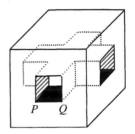

16. A rectangle with vertices $A(-6, 1)$, $B(-2, 1)$, $C(-2, 7)$, and $D(-6, 7)$ is rotated $45°$ clockwise about the point $(-6, 1)$. What is the area of the portion of this rectangle that lies above the x-axis?

17. Line segments AC and BD intersect at point $P(4, 6)$, with A, B, C, and D on the axes as shown, and $OA > OB$. If the area of $\triangle AOC = 54$ and the area of $\triangle BOD = 48$, find the area of $\triangle PCD$.

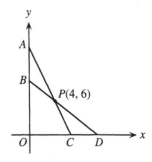

18. In triangle ABC, R is the mid-point of BC, $CS = 3SA$, and $\dfrac{AT}{TB} = \dfrac{p}{q}$. If w is the area of $\triangle CRS$, x is the area of $\triangle RBT$, z is the area of $\triangle ATS$, and $x^2 = wz$, find the value of $\dfrac{p}{q}$.

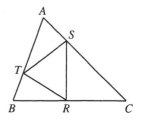

19. If $i^2 = -1$ and $p^3 = 5 + \sqrt{2}i$ and $q^3 = 5 - \sqrt{2}i$, find an integer value for $p + q$.

20. If x is a number which satisfies $\sqrt[3]{x+9} - \sqrt[3]{x-9} = 3$, find the value of x^2.

21. A fly lands on the outside of a cylindrical drinking glass 6 cm from the top. Diametrically opposite the fly and 7 cm from the bottom, but on the inside of the glass, there is a drop of honey. The glass has circumference 24 cm, height 10 cm and negligible thickness. Find the shortest path, in cm, that the fly must walk to reach the honey.

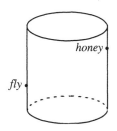

22. AB is the diameter, length two, of a semi-circle with centre O. The point C lies on the semicircle and triangle ACB is isosceles. If T is a point on CB, find the radius of the circle of maximum area with diameter TR, where R lies on the semi-circle.

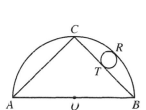

23. AB is the diameter, length two, of a semicircle with centre O. The points C, D, and E are on the semicircle with F and G being points on BC. If triangle ABC is isosceles, and $DEFG$ is a square, determine the area of $DEFG$.

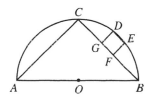

Solutions

Chapter 1 *Solutions*

1. *Solution*
   Let the end have sides x units.
   Then the sides are length $x + 3$ units.
   The area of each end is x^2.
   The area of each of the four sides is

   $x(x+3) = x^2 + 3x$.

   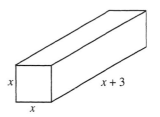

   Then $\quad 2x^2 + 4(x^2 + 3x) = 210$

   $\qquad 6x^2 + 12x - 210 = 0$.

   Dividing by 6, $\quad x^2 + 2x - 35 = 0$

   $\qquad\qquad (x+7)(x-5) = 0$

   $\qquad\qquad x = -7 \text{ or } x = 5$.

   But x cannot be -7, so $x = 5$.
   The dimensions of the block are 5 by 5 by 8 units.

2. *Solution*
   From the first three terms we get $a^2 + 3ab + 2b^2 - (a+b)(a+2b)$.
   Hence $a^2 + 3ab + 2b^2 - 10a - 20b = (a+b)(a+2b) - 10(a+2b)$

   $$= (a+2b)(a+b-10).$$

   If $(a+2b)(a+b-10) = 0$, then $a+2b = 0$ or $a+b-10 = 0$.
   But if a and b are positive integers, $a+2b \neq 0$.
   Hence $a+b-10 = 0$ or $a+b = 10$.
   In positive integers we can have $(a, b) = (1, 9), (2, 8), \cdots, (8, 2), (9, 1)$.
   There are 8 pairs of positive integers that satisfy the equation.

3. *Solution*
   Since there are twelve months, the first twelve people could conceivably have their
   birthdays in different months, but the thirteenth person must have a birthday in the same
   month as one of the first twelve people.

   This is an application of the Pigeonhole Principle, which states that if there are m
   receptables and $m+1$ objects to be placed in the m receptables, at least one receptable
   will receive more than one object.
   Question: Can you make any further statement about the fourteen people?

4. *Solution*
   You can easily guess at the correct answer. If $n = 11^2 = 121$, then $n + 23 = 144 = 12^2$.
   But you can't be sure that this is the only value for n without some mathematical proof.
   Here's a good way to go at it.

Let $n = p^2$.

Then $n + 23 = q^2$ where p and q are positive integers.

Hence $q^2 - p^2 = 23$.

Then $(q - p)(q + p) = 23$.

But 23 is a prime number, so it can be expressed as a product of two numbers only as 23×1. Also $q + p$ is greater than $q - p$, so we write

$$q + p = 23$$
$$q - p = 1$$
$$2q = 24$$
$$q = 12$$
$$p = 11.$$

Then $n = 11^2 = 121$ and this is the only possible value for n.

5. *Solution 1*

There are n people present, so each of them shakes $(n - 1)$ hands.

There are, then, $n(n - 1)$ handshakes, but this counts each handshake twice.

The actual number of handshakes is $\frac{1}{2}n(n - 1)$.

Then $\frac{1}{2}n(n - 1) = 28$

$$n^2 - n = 56.$$

By inspection, $n = 8$.

There are 8 persons present.

Solution 2

If the first person shakes the hand of all others, $(n - 1)$ handshakes are required.

If the second person then shakes the hand of all except the first person, $(n - 2)$ handshakes are required.

The third person then shakes hands with $(n - 3)$ persons, and so on, until the second last person shakes hands only with the last person.

The number of handshakes is $(n - 1) + (n - 2) + (n - 3) + \cdots + 3 + 2 + 1$, and by pairing the first and last, second and second last, and so on, there are $n - 1$ numbers with an average of $\frac{n}{2}$.

Hence the total number of handshakes is $\dfrac{n(n - 1)}{2}$.

Then $\dfrac{n(n - 1)}{2} = 28$

$$n^2 - n = 56.$$

By inspection, $n = 8$.

There were 8 persons present.

6.   *Solution*

If $x^2 + 3x + 8$ is a factor of $x^4 + rx^2 + s$, let the other factor be $x^2 + px + q$.

Then $\left(x^2 + 3x + 8\right)\left(x^2 + px + q\right) = x^4 + rx^2 + s$

or $x^4 + (3 + p)x^3 + (8 + 3p + q)x^2 + (8p + 3q)x + 8q = x^4 + rx^2 + s$.

This is possible only if $p + 3 = 0$

$$8 + 3p + q = r$$
$$8p + 3q = 0$$
$$8q = s.$$

If $p + 3 = 0$, then $p = -3$.

If $p = -3$, then $8(-3) + 3q = 0$ and $q = 8$.

If $p = -3, q = 8$, then $8 + 3p + q = r = 7$ and $8q = 64 = s$.

Then $r = 7$ and $s = 64$.

7.   *Solution*

Because $PA = PD = PE$, if EP is extended to meet
AD at F it is perpendicular to AD and divides AD
in two equal parts.

Let the side of the square be $2x$ units.
(Note that by using $2x$ for the side, we avoid
fractions in considering AF).

Then $AF = x$ and $PF = 2x - 10$, and $x > 5$.

In triangle APF, $(PA)^2 = (AF)^2 + (PF)^2$

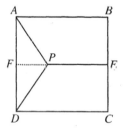

$$100 = x^2 + (2x - 10)^2$$
$$100 = x^2 + 4x^2 - 40x + 100$$
$$5x^2 - 40x = 0$$
$$5x(x - 8) = 0.$$

Then $x = 0$ or $x = 8$.

Hence the side of the square is 16 and its area is 256.

8.   *Solution*

By Pythagoras, if $AB = 12$ and $AD = 9$, then $DB = 15$.

Let DP be x units. (This is better than letting PQ be x, because we avoid fractions).

Then $PQ = 15 - 2x$ and $PB = 15 - x$.

Using Pythagoras in triangles APD and APB, we obtain $AP^2 = 9^2 - x^2$ and
$AP^2 = 12^2 - (15 - x)^2$.

Then $12^2 - (15 - x)^2 = 9^2 - x^2$

$(15 - x)^2 - x^2 = 12^2 - 9^2$ (and we can factor on both sides)

$$(15 - x - x)(15 - x + x) = (12 - 9)(12 + 9)$$
$$(15 - 2x)15 = 3 \times 21$$
$$(15 - 2x)5 = 21$$
$$75 - 10x = 21$$
$$10x = 54$$
$$x = 5.4.$$

Then $PQ = 15 - 10.8 = 4.2$ units.

9. *Solution*

Assigning coordinates to D of $(0, 0)$ and C of $(8, 0)$, R is the point $(2, 1)$, Q is $(4, 2)$, and P is $(6, 3)$. The image of R in DC is $T(2, -1)$. If the ball at P is sent toward $T(2, -1)$ it will bounce at point $V(k, 0)$ to point T because

$$\angle PVC = \angle DVT = \angle DVR.$$

Then slope $PV =$ slope PT

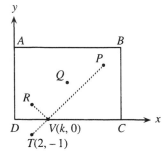

or $\dfrac{3}{6 - k} = \dfrac{3 + 1}{6 - 2} = \dfrac{1}{1}.$

Then $3 = 6 - k$
$k = 3.$

The ball at P should strike the edge at the point $(3, 0)$ or 3 units from D.

10. *Solution*

The product of a set of integers is even if one or more of the integers is even. Hence we must prove that at least one of the brackets gives an even integer.

A bracket will be even if it contains two even integers or if it contains two odd integers.

There are ten odd integers in the set $\{31, 32, \cdots, 49\}$ and there are only nine brackets in which an even number is to be subtracted from the a_k used.

Therefore there must be one bracket in which there are two odd integers, and the difference between them is even.

Therefore there is always at least one even integer in the product and the product is even.

11. *Solution*

There are 24 street blocks and 16 vertices where streets meet. Of these vertices, 4 have four streets, 4 have two streets, and 8 have three streets meeting at them.

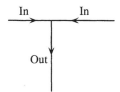

If a vertex has an even number of streets, one can always come to the vertex and leave it along an unused street, or leave it and return along an unused street. However, if there are an odd number of streets meeting at a vertex, then one ultimately must leave along a street already used, as illustrated.

Note that the second time one comes the vertex, it is necessary to leave by going along a street already walked. Since there are four pairs of such vertices, the minimal number of streets that must be used twice is 4.

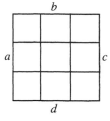

These streets are labelled *a*, *b*, *c*, and *d*.

It is now possible to cover the entire route by walking 28 street blocks.

12. *Solution*

(a) Since region *g* has an edge in common with four regions (a, c, d, f), *g* cannot be 3, 4, or 5, since none of these has four integers differing by at least 2 in the set. Hence *g* can be 1, 2, 6, or 7.

If *g* is 1, then *b* or *e* must be 2, and since it doesn't matter which, we put $b = 2$. Then we can set $d = 3$, $f = 4$, $a = 5$, $c = 6$, $e = 7$, and we see that it is possible.

If *g* is 2, an assignment that satisfies is $b = 1$, $e = 3$, $c = 4$, $f = 6$, $a = 5$ and $d = 7$.

For $g = 6$ or $g = 7$, we note that replacing any number *t* by $8 - t (g = 7, b = 6,$ etc.) will provide a suitable assignment.

Hence there are four acceptable values that can be assigned to *g*.

(b) If the numbers in each region are to differ by more than 2, then *g* must be 1 or 7.

If *g* is 1, we must put 4, 5, 6, 7 in regions *a*, *c*, *d*, *e*, but this forces *b* and *e* to be 2 and 3, and this is not allowed.

Symmetrically, if *g* is 7, then 1, 2, 3, 4 must be assigned to regions *a*, *c*, *d*, *e*, and this forces *b* and *e* to be 5 and 6. Again, this is not possible.

We conclude that it is impossible to assign the integers so that numbers in adjacent regions differ by more than 2.

Chapter 2   *Solutions*

1. *Solution 1*
    First we should evaluate inside the bracket.

    $$16 - 14(16 - 14) = 16 - 14(2)$$
    $$= 16 - 28$$
    $$= -12.$$

    Solution 2
    We could start by distributing 14 over the terms in the bracket.
    Thus, $16 - 14(16 - 14) = 16 - 14 \times 16 - 14(-14)$

    $$= 16 - 224 + 196$$
    $$= 212 - 224$$
    $$= -12.$$

2. *Solution 1*
    $$2\frac{1}{10} + 3\frac{11}{100} + 4\frac{111}{1000} = 2 + \frac{1}{10} + 3 + \frac{11}{100} + 4 + \frac{111}{1000}.$$

    Regrouping we get $2 + 3 + 4 + \frac{1}{10} + \frac{11}{100} + \frac{111}{1000}$

    $$= 9 + \frac{100}{1000} + \frac{110}{1000} + \frac{111}{1000}$$
    $$= 9 + \frac{321}{1000}$$
    $$= 9\frac{321}{1000}$$
    $$= 9.321.$$

    Solution 2
    $$2\frac{1}{10} + 3\frac{11}{100} + 4\frac{111}{1000} = 2.1 + 3.11 + 4.111$$
    $$= 9.321.$$

3. *Solution 1*
    Multiply each term in the numerator and denominator by 21 to get

    $$\frac{21\left(\frac{3}{7} - 1\right)}{21\left(1 - \frac{7}{3}\right)} = \frac{9 - 21}{21 - 49}$$
    $$= \frac{-12}{-28}$$
    $$= \frac{3}{7}.$$

    Why do we choose to multiply by 21?

Solution 2

$$\frac{\frac{3}{7}-1}{1-\frac{7}{3}} = \frac{\frac{3}{7}-\frac{7}{7}}{\frac{3}{3}-\frac{7}{3}}$$

$$= \frac{-\frac{4}{7}}{-\frac{4}{3}}$$

$$= \left(-\frac{4}{7}\right)\left(-\frac{3}{4}\right)$$

$$= \frac{3}{7}.$$

4.   *Solution*
     Since 268 is the result of subtracting 189 from 4 ♥ 7, then 4 ♥ 7 must represent the sum of 189 and 268.
     Since $189 + 268 = 457$, 4 ♥ 7 must represent 457 so the ♥ symbol is 5.

5.   *Solution 1*
     Let us undo the processes in the reverse order.
     If the number was tripled to get 96, the previous number was $\frac{96}{3} = 32$.
     Since 32 was increased by 12, the previous number was $32 - 12 = 20$.
     Since the original number was doubled to give 20, then the original number was $\frac{20}{2} = 10$.

     Solution 2
     If x was the original number, then $3\lfloor 2(x) + 12 \rfloor = 96$

     $$3(2x + 12) = 96$$
     $$2x + 12 = 32$$
     $$2x = 20$$
     $$x = 10.$$

     The original number was 10.

6.   *Solution*
     Since there are five integers, and since the sum of the first three and the sum of the last three are calculated, the third integer must be repeated.
     Since the middle integer is repeated in each sum, we only need to calculate the sums of the first two and of the last two integers.
     We could find the sums of all pairs of integers but by observation we see that
     $8 + 15 = 23 = 19 + 4$.
     Since 8, 15, 19, and 4 are used, the middle integer is 3.

7.   *Solution*
     You should realize that the product of an odd number of negative integers results in an odd integer and that the product of an even number of odd integers results in an even integer.

$$(1)^{10} + (-1)^8 + (-1)^7 + (1)^5 = 1 + (+1) + (-1) + 1$$
$$= 1 + 1 - 1 + 1$$
$$= 2.$$

8.   *Solution*

$$\sqrt{3^2 + 4^2 + 12^2} = \sqrt{9 + 16 + 144}$$
$$= \sqrt{169}$$
$$= 13.$$

Why is $\sqrt{3^2 + 4^2 + 12^2}$ not equal to $3 + 4 + 12$?

9.   *Solution*
     Evaluating the inner root first, we get $\sqrt{7 + \sqrt{4}} = \sqrt{7 + 2} = \sqrt{9} = 3$.
     Why is -3 not a correct result?

10. *Solution 1*
     If the number is tripled when 24 is added to it, then the number must represent one third of the final result and 24 must represent two thirds of this result.
     Thus the number must be one half of 24 or 12.

     Solution 2
     If x is the original number, then $24 + x = 3x$

$$24 = 2x$$
$$x = 12.$$

     The original number is 12.

11. *Solution*
     Since $3^2 \times 3^3 \times 3^4$ has each power written with the same base, its value is $3^{2+3+4} = 3^9$.

     Alternatively, $3^9 = \left(3^3\right)^3 = 27^3$, or $3^9 = \left(3^2\right)^{\frac{9}{2}} = 9^{\frac{9}{2}}$.

     Many forms of the answer are possible; it depends on which base is desired.

12. *Solution*
     If we regroup $\left(12.5 \times 10^{-3}\right) \times \left(8 \times 10^{111}\right)$, we get $(12.5 \times 8) \times \left(10^{-3} \times 10^{111}\right) = 100 \times 10^{108}$

$$= 10^2 \times 10^{108}$$
$$= 10^{110}.$$

13. *Solution 1*
     Squaring both sides of the equation gives $x + 9 = 81$
     $$x = 72.$$

     Solution 2
     Since the result of taking the square root is 9, the original number must have been 81.
     Therefore $x + 9 = 81$
     $$x = 72.$$

14. *Solution*
     We could eliminate fractions by multiplying each term by 30 which is the lowest common multiple of 15 and 30.
     $$30\left(\frac{8}{15}\right) + 30\left(\frac{7}{30}\right) = 30\left(\frac{x}{30}\right)$$
     $$2(8) + 7 = x$$
     $$16 + 7 = x$$
     $$x = 23.$$

     Alternatively, we could first add the fractions on the left side of the equation to give $\frac{23}{30} = \frac{x}{30}$.
     The value of x is 23.
     Usually it is advantageous to eliminate fractions at the start of the solution.

15. *Solution*
     Since these powers are not easy to evaluate (even with a calculator) we look for a better way.
     If we notice 4 and 8 are both powers of 2, we might consider changing the bases.
     $$4^{31} \div 8^{17} = \left(2^2\right)^{31} \div \left(2^3\right)^{17}$$
     $$= 2^{62} \div 2^{51}$$
     $$= 2^{11}$$
     $$= 2048.$$

16. *Solution*
     $$\left(3^a\right)\left(3^b\right)\left(3^c\right) = 243$$
     $$3^{a+b+c} = 243 = 3^5.$$
     Thus, $a + b + c = 5$.

     The average of a, b, and c is $\dfrac{a+b+c}{3} = \dfrac{5}{3}$.

17. *Solution*

Since $\sqrt{10} \doteq 3.1$ and $\sqrt{110} \doteq 10.4$ we want the number of integers larger than -3.1 and smaller than 10.4.

A number line helps to see the solution.

Since -3.1 is smaller than -3, then -3 is included in our list.

The integers are $-3, -2, -1, 0, 1, 2, 3, 4, 5, 6, 7, 8, 9, 10$, giving a total of 14 integers in the set.

Notice that $10 - (-3) = 13$ does not produce the correct answer, since you are not including -3 in the set.

In general, if we want the number of integers between a and b (where a and b are integers with $b > a$), the answer is $b - a + 1$.

18. *Solution*

To find the largest prime factor we must find the prime decomposition of 1995. Here is a useful pattern for doing this:

$$
\begin{array}{r|r}
5 & 1995 \\ \hline
3 & 399 \\ \hline
7 & 133 \\ \hline
& 19
\end{array}
$$

The only prime factors of 1995 are 3, 5, 7, and 19.
Therefore the largest prime factor is 19.

19. *Solution*

Since $6 = 2 \times 3$, the divisors of 6 are 1, 2, 3, and 6.

The sum of their reciprocals is $\dfrac{1}{1} + \dfrac{1}{2} + \dfrac{1}{3} + \dfrac{1}{6} = \dfrac{6 + 3 + 2 + 1}{6}$

$$= \frac{12}{6}$$

$$= 2.$$

Notice that the prime decomposition of 6 produces 2 and 3, but that the divisors of 6 include 1 and 6.

20. *Solution*

Since 50 letters are stamped in 60 seconds, the machine can stamp one letter in $\dfrac{6}{5}$ seconds.

Therefore $\dfrac{6}{5}(80) = 96$ seconds are required to stamp 80 letters.

21. *Solution 1*
    Athos paid $21.00 for the stamp.
    Rafeena made a profit of $4.00 so she must have paid $21.00 − $4.00 = $17.00.
    Chris lost $2.00 so he must have paid $17.00 + $2.00 = $19.00.
    Sandy had made a profit of $5.00, so she must have paid $19.00 − $5.00 = $14.00.

    Solution 2
    Suppose Sandy had paid x dollars for the stamp.
    Chris then must have paid $x + 5$.
    Rafeena must have paid $(x + 5) - 2 = (x + 3)$.
    Athos must have paid $(x + 3) + 4 = (x + 7)$.
    But Athos paid $21.00 so $x + 7 = 21$
    $$x = 14.$$
    Sandy paid $14 for the stamp.
    Many questions can be done using either an arithmetic or an algebraic approach.

22. *Solution*
    One way to compare fractions is to write them all with a common denominator and then
    write them in order.
    Changing all the denominators to 30, we get $\frac{10}{30} < \frac{k}{30} < \frac{12}{30}$.
    The value of k must be larger than 10 and also less than 12.
    The only possible value of k is 11.

23. *Solution*
    To get the largest fraction, we need the maximum value in the numerator divided by the
    minimum value in the denominator.
    Thus we should use the largest value for x and the least value for y.
    The maximum value of $\frac{x^2}{2y}$ is $\frac{(20)^2}{2(40)} = \frac{400}{80} = 5$.

24. *Solution*
    Since any negative number is less than any positive number, we choose a positive number
    multiplied by a negative number.
    To minimize the result we select -9 and 6.
    The least possible value of the product is $-9 \times 6 = -54$.

25. *Solution*
    The total amount spent on the dinner is $8.43 + $13.37 + $2.46 = $24.26.
    Half of the cost of the dinner is $\frac{\$24.26}{2} = \$12.13$.
    Pat owes $12.13 − $2.46 = $9.67.
    Avoid using an algebraic solution for this type of problem. It is best done using arithmetic
    reasoning.

26. *Solution*

    Since there is an equal number of each kind of coin, it would be advisable to determine what the value of a package consisting of one of each coin.

    Since $1 + 5 + 10 + 25 + 100 = 141$, each package of one of each of the coins would amount to $1.41.

    How many such packages are possible?

    Since $4 \times 41 = 564$, there are 4 packages of sets of 5 coins each.

    Thus the total number of coins in the bank is $5 \times 4 = 20$.

27. *Solution*

    There are 10 coins consisting of nickels, dimes and quarters.

    If 7 of the coins are either dimes or quarters, the remaining 3 must be nickels.

    If 8 of the coins are either dimes or nickels, the remaining 2 must be quarters.

    If there are 3 nickels and 2 quarters, the remaining 5 must be dimes.

    Janet has 5 dimes.

    Note: Algebraic equations could have been set up using the number of each kind of coin as a variable. This would have resulted in 3 equations in 3 unknowns which could be solved fairly easily. However this method looks like overkill. Look before you leap.

28. *Solution 1*

    Let x dollars be the amount that Amy spent.

    Then Cathy spent $2x$ dollars.

    $$4.50 - 2x = \frac{1}{2}(3.00 - x)$$
    $$9 - 4x = 3 - x$$
    $$3x = 6.$$

    The total amount spent by both girls is 6 dollars.

    Solution 2

    Trial and error (with thought) is an acceptable way to solve problems.

    Cathy can spend up to $4.50, but it must be more than $1.50 or her amount would not be less than Amy's.

    Let us try $2 as the amount Cathy spent. Then Cathy has $2.50 left and Amy has $3 – $1 = $2.00 left.

    But the amount Cathy has left is not one-half as much as Amy has.

    Let us try $4 as the amount Cathy spent.

    Now Cathy has $4.50 – $4.00 = $0.50 left and Amy has $3.00 – $2.00 = $1.00 left.

    Amy now has twice as much money left as Cathy has.

    Voilà! We have the answer.

    The girls spent a total of $4.00 + $2.00 = 6.00.

29. *Solution 1*

Since 80% of the weeds are killed, 20% must still be left.

After the first spraying $\frac{20}{100} \times 275 = 55$ weeds remain.

After the second spraying $\frac{20}{100} \times 55 = 11$ weeds remain.

This result could have been obtained by calculating $275 \times \frac{20}{100} \times \frac{20}{100} = 11$.

Solution 2

After one spraying $\frac{80}{100} \times 275 = 220$ weeds are killed.

The number of weeds remaining is $275 - 220 = 55$.

After the second spraying $\frac{80}{100} \times 55 = 44$ weeds are killed.

The number of weeds now remaining is $55 - 44 = 11$.

30. *Solution*

If the population of Sudbury was x at the start of 1996, then the population at the end of the year was $\frac{94}{100} x$.

If the population of Victoria was y at the start of 1996, at the end of the year it was $\frac{114}{100} y$.

Therefore $\frac{94}{100} x = \frac{114}{100} y$

$$94x = 114y$$

$$\frac{x}{y} = \frac{114}{94}$$

$$= \frac{57}{47}.$$

The ratio of the populations at the beginning of 1996 was 57:47.

31. *Solution 1*

If the ratio of water to vinegar is 2:1, then $\frac{2}{3}$ of the mixture is water and $\frac{1}{3}$ vinegar.

If the first jar held 12 units, then 8 units would be water and 4 units would be vinegar.
The second jar holds twice as much, so it contains 24 units.

Since $\frac{3}{4}$ of the second jar is water, it contains 18 units of water and 6 units of vinegar.

The third container holds $8 + 18 = 26$ units of water and $4 + 6 = 10$ units of vinegar.
The ratio of water to vinegar is $26 : 10 = 13 : 5$.
Why did we use 12 units in the first jar? Could we have used other values? Would the work have been easier?

Solution 2

Let the first jar hold $2x$ units of water and x units of vinegar.

Let the second jar hold $3y$ units of water and y units of vinegar.

The first jar holds $3x$ units and the second jar $4y$ units.

The second jar holds twice the volume of the first so $4y = 2(3x)$ or $y = \frac{3}{2}x$.

The third container contains $2x + 3y$ units of water and $x + y$ units of vinegar.

The ratio of water to vinegar now is
$$\frac{2x + 3y}{x + y} = \frac{2x + 3\left(\frac{3}{2}x\right)}{x + \frac{3}{2}x}$$

$$= \frac{\frac{13x}{2}}{\frac{5}{2}x}$$

$$= \frac{13}{5} \text{ or } 13:5.$$

32.   *Solution 1*

If the sum of the nine integers is 99, the average is $\frac{99}{9} = 11$.

Since the integers are consecutive, 11 must be in the middle and so there are four integers above 11 and four below 11.

The fourth integer above 11 is $11 + 4 = 15$.

The largest number is 15.

Solution 2

If we call the middle integer x, then the four integers above are $x+1, x+2, x+3, x+4$ and the four below are $x-1, x-2, x-3, x-4$.

Thus, $(x-4)+(x-3)+(x-2)+(x-1)+(x)+(x+1)+(x+2)+(x+3)+(x+4) = 99$.

This gives $9x = 99$

$$x = 11$$

and so $x + 4 = 15$.

The largest number is 15.

33.   *Solution 1*

Since 35 805 is the product of three integers, these integers must be contained as some combinations of its prime factors.

```
 5 | 35 805
 3 |  7161
 7 |  2387
11 |   341
         31
```

Since the prime factors of 35 805 are 5, 3, 7, 11, and 31, we must find the combinations that produce three consecutive odd integers.

By trial, $5 \times 7 = 35$, $3 \times 11 = 33$ and 31 gives the correct combination.
The three odd integers are 31, 33, and 35 and their average is the middle integer or 33.

Solution 2
Since 35 805 is the product of three consecutive odd integers, the cube root of 35 805 should
be near the average of the three.

$$\sqrt[3]{35\,805} \doteq 32.9$$

Suppose the middle one is 33. The other two numbers would be 31 and 35.
Now test the product to show that it is 35 805.

34. *Solution 1*
If the average of 8 numbers is 5, then their sum is $8 \times 5 = 40$.
After the increase, there are 8 numbers with an average of 6.
The new sum is $8 \times 6 = 48$.
Since the increase in the total is 8, one number is increased by 8.

Solution 2
The sum of the original numbers is 40.
If the amount added to one number is x, then the sum is $40 + x$.

The new average is $\dfrac{40 + x}{8} = 6$.

$$40 + x = 48$$
$$x = 8.$$

The amount added to one number is 8.

35. *Solution*
If the average of a set of 20 numbers is 36, then the sum of the numbers is $20 \times 36 = 720$.
When 38 and 52 are removed, the sum of the new set of numbers is $720 - 38 - 52 = 630$.

The average of these remaining eighteen numbers is $\frac{630}{18} = 35$.

36. *Solution*
Let us list the powers that produce integers greater than 2 and less than 50, excluding
$y = 1$.

$$2^2 = 4, 2^3 = 8, 2^4 = 16, 2^5 = 32$$
$$3^2 = 9, 3^3 = 27$$

Do not use 4 since powers of 2 have already been listed.

$$5^2 = 25$$
$$6^2 = 36$$
$$7^2 = 49$$

Since the squares of other positive integers are greater than 50, our list is complete and
contains 9 integers.

37. *Solution*

If you notice that the product of x^2yz^3 and xy^2 is $x^3y^3z^3$, the problem is easy.

$$\left(x^2yz^3\right)\left(xy^2\right) = 7^3 \times 7^9$$
$$x^3y^3z^3 = 7^{12}.$$

By taking the cube root, we get $\left(x^3y^3z^3\right)^{\frac{1}{3}} = \left(7^{12}\right)^{\frac{1}{3}}$

$$xyz = 7^4.$$

38. *Solution*

We may eliminate x's and y's by adding and subtracting the equations.

Adding we get $3^x + 2^y + 3^x - 2^y = 985 + 473$

$$2\left(3^x\right) = 1458$$
$$3^x = 729$$
$$= 3^6.$$

Therefore $x = 6$.

Similarly, $3^x + 2^y - 3^x + 2^y = 985 - 473$

$$2\left(2^y\right) = 512$$
$$2^y = 256$$
$$= 2^8$$
$$y = 8.$$

The sum of x and y is $6 + 8 = 14$.

Note: If, in the solution, you did not recognize that 729 is a power of 3, you could have written $3^x = 729$ and then taken logarithms of both sides to get $x \log 3 = \log 729$.

From this, $x = \dfrac{\log 729}{\log 3}$ and you could use your calculator to find x. A similar procedure would allow you to obtain y. This would not be a very pretty solution.

39. *Solution*

By factoring the numerator and denominator, we get $\dfrac{2^{1990} - 2^{1989}}{2^{1990} + 2^{1989}} = \dfrac{2^{1989}(2 - 1)}{2^{1989}(2 + 1)}$

$$= \frac{2 - 1}{2 + 1}$$
$$= \frac{1}{3}.$$

40. *Solution*

A natural first step seems to be to take square roots in each equation.
Remember that square roots produce two values, positive and negative.
Thus, $x + y = \pm 4$

$$y + z = \pm 6$$

and $z + x = \pm 9$.

We could solve for x, y and z using simultaneous pairs of equations. What a horrible thought!

Notice that the question does not ask for the values of x, y and z.

If we add, we get $(x + y) + (y + z) + (z + x) = \pm 4, \pm 6, \pm 9$.

This produces $2x + 2y + 2z = +19, 11, 7, 1, -1, -7, -11$ or -19

$$2(x + y + z) = 19, 11 \text{ or } 7.$$

We can neglect the others since the results would not be greater than 3.

The three possible values of $x + y + z$ are $\frac{19}{2}, \frac{11}{2}$, and $\frac{7}{2}$.

41. *Solution*

$$6^{x+2} - 6^x = 210\sqrt{6}$$

$$\left(6^2\right)\left(6^x\right) - 6^x = 210 \times 6^{\frac{1}{2}}$$

$$6^x\left(6^2 - 1\right) = 210 \times 6^{\frac{1}{2}}$$

$$6^x(35) = 210 \times 6^{\frac{1}{2}}$$

$$6^x = \frac{210}{35} \times 6^{\frac{1}{2}}$$

$$6^x = 6^1 \times 6^{\frac{1}{2}}$$

$$= 6^{\frac{3}{2}}.$$

Therefore $x = \frac{3}{2}$.

Then $6^{2x-1} = 6^{2\left(\frac{3}{2}\right)-1}$

$$= 6^2$$

$$= 36.$$

42. *Solution*

Since $2^{6.5} = a$ and $3^{7.5} = b$, then $6^{9.5}$ may be written as $(2 \times 3)^{9.5} = 2^{9.5} \times 3^{9.5}$.

Since $2^{9.5} = 2^{6.5} \times 2^3$ and $3^{9.5} = 3^{7.5} \times 3^2$, then $6^{9.5}$ may be written as

$2^{6.5} \times 2^3 \times 3^{7.5} \times 3^2$ which equals $a \times 8 \times b \times 9$ or $72ab$.

43. *Solution*

In a perfect square each prime factor must occur an even number of times.

Rewriting $2^9 \times 3^{14} \times 5^{15} \times 6^3$, we get $2^9 \times 3^{14} \times 5^{15} \times 2^3 \times 3^3$

$$= 2^{12} \times 3^{16} \times 5^{14} \times 3 \times 5.$$

For the whole quantity to be a perfect square, the smallest integer we must multiply by is $3 \times 5 = 15$.

By doing so, every prime factor will occur an even number of times.

44. *Solution*

These numbers are too large to calculate easily so perhaps we can operate on each in the same manner and then arrange in order.

Since 666, 555, 444, 333 and 222 are all multiples of 111, we could take the 111th root of each and then check the results.

$$\left(3^{666}\right)^{\frac{1}{111}} = 3^6 = 729$$

$$\left(4^{555}\right)^{\frac{1}{111}} = 4^5 = 1024$$

$$\left(5^{444}\right)^{\frac{1}{111}} = 5^4 = 625$$

$$\left(6^{333}\right)^{\frac{1}{111}} = 6^3 = 216$$

$$\left(7^{222}\right)^{\frac{1}{111}} = 7^2 = 49$$

The magnitude of the 111th roots are now apparent so the original numbers, in descending order of magnitude, are $4^{555}, 3^{666}, 5^{444}, 6^{333}, 7^{222}$.

45. *Solution 1*

Each even integer is one more than the preceding odd integer.

Then the sum of the even integers is the sum of the odd integers plus 1 extra for each integer or, in this case, $50^2 + 50(1) = 2550$.

Solution 2

The sum of the first 50 odd integers and the first fifty even integers is the sum of the integers from 1 to 100.

This sum is $1+2+3+...+99+100 = \dfrac{100 \times 101}{2} = 5050.$

The sum of the even integers will be the total sum minus the sum of the odd integers.

Therefore the sum of the first 50 even integers is $5050 - 50^2 = 5050 - 2500$
$$= 2550.$$

46. *Solution*

Since there is seemingly no pattern to the sums of the terms we must extend the sequence.

$t_1 = 6, t_2 = 14, t_3 = 14 - 6 = 8, t_4 = 8 - 14 = -6, \ t_5 = -6 - 8 = -14, t_6 = -14 - (-6) = -8,$

$t_7 = -8 - (-14) = 6, \ t_8 = 6 - (-8) = 14, t_9 = 14 - 6 = 8, t_{10} = 8 - 14 = -6,$ etc.

Now we begin to see a pattern; the sequence repeats itself after a set of six terms.

The sum of each set of six terms is $6 + 14 + 8 + (-6) + (-14) + (-8) = 0.$

How many sets of six are there?

Since $2000 - 6(333) + 2$ we need the sum of 333 sets of 6, plus two extra terms.

Therefore the sum of 2000 terms is $333 \times 0 + 6 + 14 = 20.$

Chapter 3   Solutions

1. *Solution*
    The perimeter of the rectangle can be expressed as
    $2(x+1)+2(x-1)$.
    Since we know that the perimeter is 24,
    then $2(x+1)+2(x-1)=24$
    $$4x = 24$$
    $$x = 6.$$

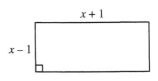

2. *Solution*
    The area of the rectangle is $9 \times 7 = 63$.
    The four corner triangles are congruent, each
    having area $\frac{1}{2}(2)(2)=2$.
    Thus the area of the shaded region is
    $63 - 4(2) = 55$.

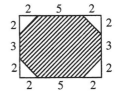

3. *Solution*
    If the area of a square is 484 cm^2, then the length of each side of the square
    is $\sqrt{484} = 22$ cm.
    The perimeter is $4(22) = 88$ cm.

4. *Solution*
    Since the formula for the circumference of any circle is $c = \pi d$, where d is the diameter of
    that circle, then the ratio of the circumference to the diameter of any circle is always $\pi:1$.

5. *Solution*
    Let the radius of the circle be r cm.
    Then $2\pi r = \pi r^2$
    $$r = 2.$$
    The radius of the circle is 2 cm.

6. *Solution*
    The area of the n circles is $n\pi\left(\frac{1}{2}\right)^2 = \frac{n\pi}{4}$.

    Therefore $\frac{n\pi}{4} = 9\pi$
    $$n = 36.$$

7.   *Solution 1*
      The shaded region is made up of four triangles of
      equal area, each with a base and height of one unit.
      Therefore the area of the shaded region is

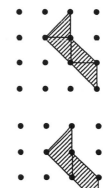

$$4\left(\frac{1}{2}\right)(1)(1)=2.$$

      Solution 2
      The shaded area may be broken into a triangle with
      base 2 and height 1, and a parallelogram with base 1
      and height 1.

      Therefore the area is $\left(\frac{1}{2}\right)(1)(1)+(1)(1)=1+1=2$.

8.   *Solution*
      Let the depth of each cut be d.
      Then $80(15)-5d-15d-10d = 990$

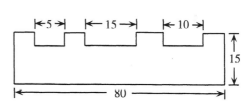

$$1200-30d = 990$$
$$-30d = -210$$
$$d = 7.$$

      The depth of each cut is 7.

9.   *Solution*
      Let the sides of the squares each have length x.
      Then the dimensions of the small rectangles are x
      and $2x$.
      Since the total area of $PQRS$ is 150, then

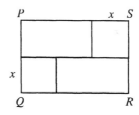

$$2\left(x^2\right)+2(x)(2x) = 150$$
$$6x^2 = 150$$
$$x = 5.$$

      The perimeter of $PQRS$ is $2(10)+2(15) = 50$.

10.   *Solution*
      If Ruby builds a solid cube with sides of length 5, she will use $5^3 = 125$ of the identical
      cubes.
      There will be $131-125 = 6$ cubes left over.

11. *Solution*
     Join AC.

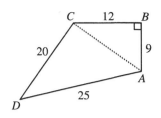

Since $\triangle ABC$ is right-angled, $AC = \sqrt{144 + 81}$
$$= \sqrt{225}$$
$$= 15.$$

Since $15^2 + 20^2 = 625 = 25^2$, $\angle DCA = 90°$.

Hence the area of quadrilateral $ABCD$ is

$$\triangle ADC + \triangle ABC = \frac{1}{2}(20)(15) + \frac{1}{2}(12)(9)$$
$$= 150 + 54$$
$$= 204.$$

12. *Solution 1*
     Since the length of each side of the smaller square is one-half the length of each side of the larger square, the area of the smaller square is one-quarter the area of the larger square.
     Therefore the ratio of the shaded area to the area of the larger square is 3:4.

     Solution 2
     Rotate and translate the smaller square as shown.
     The ratio of the shaded area to the area of the larger square is 3:4.

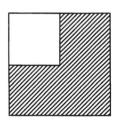

     Solution 3
     Let the length of each side of the larger square be 2.
     Then the length of each side of the smaller square is 1.
     The ratio of the shaded area to the area of the larger square is $(4-1):4 = 3:4$.

13. *Solution 1*
     Let WZ have length $2x$. Thus $RW = RP = x$.
     Since the area of $\triangle PXR$ is 3, we have, using the base RP,

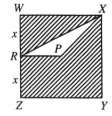

$$\frac{1}{2}(x)(x) = 3$$
$$x^2 = 6$$
$$x = \sqrt{6}.$$

     Since each side of the square has length $2x = 2\sqrt{6}$,
     the area of the square is $(2\sqrt{6})(2\sqrt{6}) = 24$.
     Hence the shaded area is $24 - 3 = 21$.

Solution 2

Extend RP to Q.

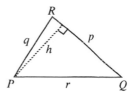

Then $\triangle XRQ = \frac{1}{2}(\text{rectangle } WRQX)$

$\qquad\quad = \frac{1}{4}(\text{square } WXYZ).$

But $\triangle RPX = \triangle XPQ$ since they have equal bases and the same heights.

Therefore $\triangle RPX = \frac{1}{4}(\text{rectangle } WRQX)$

$\qquad\qquad\quad = \frac{1}{8}(\text{square } WXYZ).$

Hence the area of square $WXYZ$ is $3 \times 8 = 24$, and so the shaded area is $24 - 3 = 21$.

14. **Solution**

The total area of the wall, in square metres, is $20 \times 60 = 1200$.

The total area of the windows, in square metres, is $20(2 \times 3) = 20 \times 6 = 120$.

The percentage of the wall made up by windows is $\frac{120}{1200} \times 100 = 10$.

15. **Solution**

Let the altitude from P be h.

Since the area of the triangle is x, $\frac{1}{2}ph = x$.

The altitude from P is $h = \dfrac{2x}{p}$.

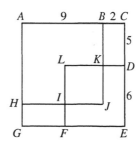

16. **Solution**

Since the area of square $ACEG$ is 121, the length of each side of $ACEG$ is 11.

Similarly, the lengths of the sides of squares $ABJH$ and $DEFL$ are 9 and 6, respectively.

$$LK = LD - KD$$
$$\quad = LD - BC$$
$$\quad = LD - (AC - AB)$$
$$\quad = 6 - (11 - 9)$$
$$\quad = 4.$$

Therefore each side of $KJIL$ is 4 and its area is $4^2 = 16$.

17. *Solution*
     If the old fish tank has width x dm, length y dm, and depth z dm, then its capacity is
     xyz dm^3 $= xyz$ litres. (Note: 1 decimetre $= 10$ cm.)
     The new fish tank will have width $2x$ dm, length $2y$ dm, and depth $2z$ dm.
     Its volume will be $(2x)(2y)(2z) = 8xyz$

     $$= 8(20)$$
     $$= 160 \text{ litres.}$$

18. *Solution*
     Since all of the shorter edges are equal in length,
     the diagram can be subdivided into 33 small
     squares, as shown.
     Each of these squares has area $\frac{528}{33} = 16$ and the
     length of each side is $\sqrt{16} = 4$.
     Counting all the sides of the squares that make up the
     perimeter of the figure, we find that the perimeter is
     $36(4) = 144$.

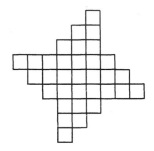

19. *Solution*
     Reshaping the pizza will not change its volume.
     The volume of the round pizza is $\pi(20)^2 \cdot 2 = 800\pi$ cm^3.
     If we let x represent the side length, in cm, of the square pizza, then this pizza has
     volume $x \cdot x \cdot 1 = x^2$.
     Therefore $x^2 = 800\pi$

     $$\doteq 2513.274.$$
     $$x \doteq \sqrt{2513.274}$$
     $$\doteq 50.1.$$

     The square pizza has side length 50 cm, to the nearest cm.

20. *Solution*
     If the length of each edge is x cm, then $x^3 = 6x^2$ and so $x = 6$.
     Since a cube has 12 edges altogether (four in each of three directions), the total length of
     all the edges is $12 \times 6 = 72$ cm.

21. *Solution*
     Since $\triangle PQS$ is a right-angled triangle, use the
     Pythagorean Theorem to get

     $$(PQ)^2 + (QS)^2 = (PS)^2$$
     $$4^2 + (QS)^2 = 5^2$$
     $$(QS)^2 = 9$$
     $$QS = 3.$$

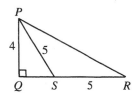

Similarly, since $\triangle PQR$ is a right-angled triangle, we get

$$(PR)^2 = (PQ)^2 + (QR)^2$$
$$= 4^2 + 8^2$$
$$= 80$$
$$PR = \sqrt{80}.$$

Thus the length of PR is $\sqrt{80}$, or approximately 8.9.

22. *Solution*
Let the width and length of the rectangle be represented by a and b respectively.

Then the length of a diagonal is $\sqrt{a^2 + b^2}$.

It is given that $a^2 + b^2 + a^2 + b^2 = 18$

$$2a^2 + 2b^2 = 18$$
$$a^2 + b^2 = 9$$

and so $\qquad \sqrt{a^2 + b^2} = 3.$

The length of a diagonal is 3.

23. *Solution*
The metrestick, the wall, and the ground will form a right-angled triangle.
Before slipping, the base of the triangle is 28 cm and the hypotenuse is 100 cm.
The height, h, of the triangle is given by

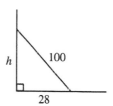

$$h = \sqrt{100^2 - 28^2}$$
$$= \sqrt{10\,000 - 784}$$
$$= \sqrt{9216}$$
$$= 96.$$

After the metrestick slips, the height of the right-angled triangle is $96 - 16 = 80$ cm.
The base, b, of the triangle is

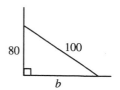

$$b = \sqrt{100^2 - 80^2}$$
$$= \sqrt{10\,000 - 6400}$$
$$= \sqrt{3600}$$
$$= 60.$$

The foot of the metrestick will slide $60 - 28 = 32$ cm.

24. *Solution*

    A cross-section through the centre of the sphere and perpendicular to the cut side of the paperweight is shown.

    If O is the centre of the sphere, then the perpendicular from O to the circular cut side meets this circle at its centre, M.

    In $\triangle OMR$, $MR = \sqrt{(OR)^2 - (OM)^2}$
    $$= \sqrt{26^2 - 10^2}$$
    $$= \sqrt{576}$$
    $$= 24.$$

    The base of the paperweight has circumference $2\pi(24) = 48\pi$ cm.

25. *Solution*

    The surface area of the closed rectangular box, in cm^2, is

    $$2(9 \times 6 + 9 \times 30 + 6 \times 30) = 2(54 + 270 + 180)$$
    $$= 2(504)$$
    $$= 1008.$$

    Let x represent the length, in cm, of an edge of the cube.

    Then the area of each of the six faces of the cube, in cm^2, is x^2.

    Therefore $6x^2 = 1008$
    $$x^2 = 168$$
    $$x = \sqrt{168}$$
    $$x \doteq 12.97$$

    The length of an edge of the cube is 13 cm, to the nearest centimetre.

26. *Solution 1*

    A side view of the swimming pool is a trapezoid with area $\frac{1}{2}(3+1)(15) = 30$ m^2.

    Therefore the volume of the swimming pool is

    $30 \times 10 = 300$ m^3.

    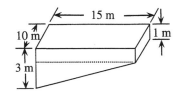

27. *Solution*

    In both diagrams X and Y, the bands must be long enough to cover four diameters plus one complete circumference of a pipe.

    Hence the bands are the same length.

    The difference in their lengths is 0.

    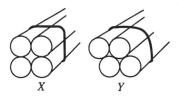

28. *Solution*

In the diagram, there are 27 black triangles.
If the entire diagram is divided into the smallest
size equilateral triangles, there are

$$8 + 2(7) + 2(6) + \ldots + 2(2) + 2(1) = 64 \text{ triangles}$$

(counting by rows). Thus, $\frac{27}{64}$ of $\triangle ABC$ is

coloured black.

Since $\triangle ABC$ is an equilateral triangle with sides of

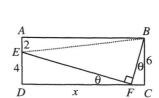

"Sierpinski Gasket"

length 16, then the area of $\triangle ABC$ is $\dfrac{\sqrt{3}(16)^2}{4}$

$$= 64\sqrt{3}.$$

Thus, the area of all the black triangles is $\frac{27}{64}\left(64\sqrt{3}\right) = 27\sqrt{3}$.

29. *Solution*

The volume of the water in the cylinder is $\pi(1)^2(2) = 2\pi$ cubic centimetres.

The volume of the three heavy spheres is $3\left[\frac{4}{3}\pi(1)^3\right] = 4\pi$ cubic centimetres.

A cylinder of radius 1 cm and volume $2\pi + 4\pi = 6\pi$ cubic centimetres has height

$$\frac{6\pi}{\pi(1)^2} = 6 \text{ cm.}$$

Then the surface of the water is 6 cm from the bottom of the cylinder. This occurs at the
top of the top sphere.

30. *Solution*

Let $CD = x$ and $CZ = y$.

Then $x^2 - y^2 = 30$ (1)

and $x^2 + y^2 = 100$.   (2)

Adding equations (1) and (2) gives

$$2x^2 = 130$$
$$x^2 = 65$$
$$x = \sqrt{65}.$$

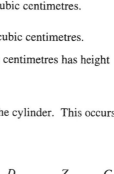

Thus the length of CD is $\sqrt{65}$.

31. *Solution*

Let $\angle EFD = \theta$.

Then $\angle BFC = 90 - \theta$ and it follows that
$\angle FBC = \theta$.

Thus $\triangle DEF$ is similar to $\triangle CFB$.

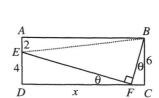

Therefore $\dfrac{BF}{BC} = \dfrac{EF}{FD}$

$$\frac{BF}{6} = \frac{\sqrt{x^2+16}}{x}$$

$$BF = \frac{\sqrt{x^2+16}}{x}.$$

The area of $\triangle BEF = \dfrac{1}{2}(EF)(BF)$

$$= \frac{1}{2}\left(\sqrt{x^2+16}\right)\left(\frac{6\sqrt{x^2+16}}{x}\right)$$

$$= \frac{3x^2+48}{x}.$$

32. *Solution*
First we require the area of the triangle. We shall use Heron's Formula.

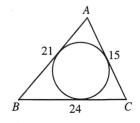

The semi-perimeter is $s = \dfrac{24+21+15}{2} = 30$.

The area of the triangle is

$$\Delta = \sqrt{30(30-24)(30-21)(30-15)}$$
$$= \sqrt{30\times6\times9\times15}$$
$$= \sqrt{24\ 300}$$
$$= 90\sqrt{3}.$$

The radius of the circle is $\dfrac{90\sqrt{3}}{30} = 3\sqrt{3}$.

The area of the inscribed circle is $\pi\left(3\sqrt{3}\right)^2 = 27\pi$.

Note: If you have studied some trigonometry, you might be interested in proving that angle $C = 60°$. Then you can calculate the area of the triangle using the formula $\Delta = \dfrac{1}{2}(24)(15)\sin 60°$.

33. *Solution*

Let the area of $\triangle PQR$ be t.

Join YP.

The areas of $\triangle YQP$ and $\triangle PQR$ are equal since they have the same height and equal bases.

Similarly, the areas of triangles YQP and YPX are equal.

Thus the area of $\triangle YQX$ is $2t$.

Similarly, the areas of triangles XPZ and YRZ are each $2t$.

Therefore $t + 2t + 2t + 2t = 420$

$$t = 60.$$

The area of $\triangle PQR$ is 60.

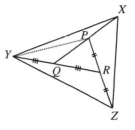

34. *Solution*

For one end of the greenhouse, complete the semi-circle as in the diagram, and let its radius be r.

Then $\triangle OBC$ is right-angled,

and $r^2 = (r-4)^2 + \left(4\sqrt{3}\right)^2$

$$r = 8.$$

Since $\triangle OBC$ has sides 4, 8, $4\sqrt{3}$, then $\angle COB = 60°$.

Hence the edge of the roof is one-third the circumference of the complete circle, or $\frac{1}{3}(16\pi)$.

The area of the roof is $\frac{1}{3}(16\pi) \times 30$ or 160π.

The area of *one* end is $\frac{1}{3}\pi 8^2 - \frac{1}{2} \cdot 8\sqrt{3} \cdot 4 = \frac{64}{3}\pi - 16\sqrt{3}$.

The total area of the roof and the ends is $\left(160\pi + \frac{128}{3}\pi - 32\sqrt{3}\right)m^2$.

35. *Solution*

(a) The astronaut can access three faces and on each of them can access an area equal to one-quarter of a circle with radius s.

Hence the surface area accessible is $\frac{3}{4}\pi s^2$.

(b) Flattening the cube out, as in the diagram, we note that the area accessible is four times sector OAB plus eight times triangle OCA. Since $OA = OB = AB = s$, $\angle AOB = 60°$ and

sector OAB is $\frac{1}{6}\pi s^2$.

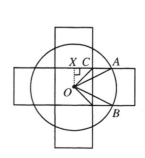

In $\triangle OCA$, the height is $\dfrac{s}{2}$ and the base AC is $XA - XC$, where $XA = \dfrac{\sqrt{3}}{2}s$ and $XC = \dfrac{s}{2}$.

The area of $\triangle OCA$ is $\dfrac{1}{8}\left(\sqrt{3}-1\right)s^2$.

The total accessible area is $4\left(\dfrac{1}{6}\pi s^2\right)+8\left(\dfrac{1}{8}\left(\sqrt{3}-1\right)s^2\right)$, or $\left(\dfrac{2}{3}\pi+\sqrt{3}-1\right)s^2$.

Chapter 4   Solutions

1. *Solution*
    To determine x, we proceed to find the value of
    $\angle BAC$ and then use the fact that $\angle EAD = 180°$.
    Since $\angle BCD = 180°$, $\angle ACB = 55°$.
    In $\triangle ABC$, $\angle BAC = 180° - 50° - 55°$
    $\qquad\qquad = 75°$.
    Hence, $\angle CAD = 180° - 80° - 75°$
    $\qquad\qquad = 25°$.
    Thus the value of x is 25.

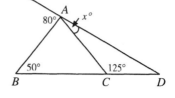

2. *Solution*
    Since $\angle BCD = 180°$, the value of x can be found
    once the value of $\angle ACB$ is known.
    In isosceles $\triangle ABC$, $\angle B = \angle ACB$
    $$= \frac{180° - 40°}{2}$$
    $$= 70°.$$
    Since $\angle BCD = 180°$, $2x = 180 - 70$
    $\qquad\qquad\qquad = 110$.
    $\qquad\qquad\quad x = 55$.
    Hence the value of x is 55.

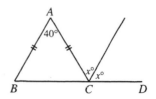

3. *Solution*
    The solution to this problem uses the sum of the
    angles in a triangle along with the fact that a and b
    are parts of two different straight angles.
    In $\triangle PQR$, $\angle QPR = 180° - 20° - 50°$
    $\qquad\qquad\qquad = 110°$.
    Since QPT is a straight angle,
    $\qquad a + 110° = 180°$
    $\qquad\qquad a = 70°$.
    Similarly, $b = 180° - 50°$
    $\qquad\qquad = 130°$.
    Hence, $a + b = 70° + 130°$
    $\qquad\qquad = 200°$.

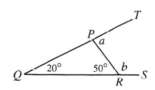

4. *Solution*
    Draw BE perpendicular to DC as shown.
    Since $AB = DE = 4$, then $EC = 2$.
    Since $\angle C = 45°$, $\angle EBC = 45°$.
    Thus triangle BEC is isosceles with
    $BE = EC = 2$.

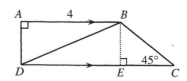

Using the Pythagorean Theorem in triangle BDE,

$$BD^2 = DE^2 + BE^2$$
$$= 4^2 + 2^2$$
$$= 20.$$

Thus $BD = \sqrt{20}$.

5. *Solution*
    Let RS be the common tangent to circles having
    centres O and P.
    Let the point of contact be Q.
    Join OQ and PQ.
    Thus $\angle OQR = 90°$ and $\angle PQR = 90°$.
    Hence $\angle OQP = 180°$.
    Thus O, Q, and P are collinear.
    Therefore the line joining the centres of tangent
    circles goes through the point of contact.
    You should prove that the result is also true when
    the two circles are tangent internally.

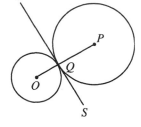

6. *Solution*
    Since triangle BAD is isosceles,
    $\angle ADB = \angle A = 52°$.
    Thus, $\angle ABD = 180° - 52° - 52$
    $\quad\quad\quad\quad = 76°$.
    Since $AB \parallel DC$ and BD is a transversal,
    $\angle BDC = \angle ABD = 76°$.
    Since triangle BDC is isosceles,
    $\angle BCD = \angle BDC = 76°$.
    It follows that $\angle DBC = 180° - 76° - 76°$
    $\quad\quad\quad\quad\quad\quad = 28°$.

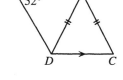

7. *Solution*
    In quadrilateral $ABCD$, $AD = BC$ and $AD \parallel BC$.
    Join BD and we get $\angle ADB = \angle DBC$.
    Since BD is common to triangles ABD and CDB,
    the triangles are congruent.
    Hence $AB = CD$ and $\angle DBA = \angle BDC$ making
    $AB \parallel CD$.

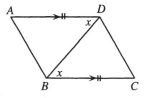

8.   *Solution*

The "shape" of the given pentagon suggests joining the points E and B to form a triangle and a quadrilateral.

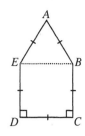

In quadrilateral $EBCD$, $ED = BC$ and $ED \parallel BC$.

Hence $EB = DC$ and $EB \parallel DC$.

Therefore $\angle DEB = \angle CBE = 90°$.

Since $\triangle AEB$ is equilateral, $\angle ABE = 60°$.

Thus $\angle ABC = 90° + 60° = 150°$.

9.   *Solution*

In order for the triangle to be isosceles, two of the sides must be equal in length. There are three cases to consider.

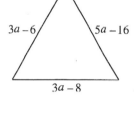

Case 1:   If $3a - 6 = 5a - 16$

$-2a = -10$

$a = 5$.

In this case, the sides of the triangle would have lengths 9, 9, and 7.

Case 2:   If $3a - 6 = 3a - 8$

$-6 = -8$.

This is not a true statement and hence this case does not result in an isosceles triangle.

Case 3:   If $5a - 16 = 3a - 8$

$2a = 8$

$a = 4$.

In this case, the sides of the triangle would have lengths 4, 4, and 6.

There are two values of a for which the given triangle would be isosceles.

10.   *Solution*

Let the centre of the circle be O.

Chord CD is the perpendicular bisector of radius OA.

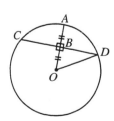

Hence $OB = BA = 4$.

Since OB is perpendicular to chord CD,

$CB = BD$.

In triangle OBD, by the Pythagorean Theorem,

$$OD^2 = OB^2 + BD^2$$

$$BD^2 = 64 - 16$$

$$= 48.$$

Therefore $BD = \sqrt{48} = 4\sqrt{3}$ and so chord CD has length $8\sqrt{3}$.

11. *Solution*

    Since D is the centre of the semicircle,

    $DB = DC = DA$.

    Since $AB = AD$, ABD is an equilateral triangle
    and so $\angle ADB = 60°$.

    Therefore $\angle ADC = 120°$.

    Since $AD = DC$, $\triangle ADC$ is isosceles and each of

    its equal angles is $\dfrac{180° - 120°}{2} = 30°$.

    Therefore $\angle ACD = 30°$.

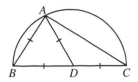

12. *Solution*

    Since the hexagon is regular, each side has length $\dfrac{21}{6} = \dfrac{7}{2}$ and each interior angle has

    measure $\dfrac{180° \times 6 - 360°}{6} = 120°$.

    Therefore each of the small triangles has base angles of $60°$ and is equilateral.

    Thus an edge of the star has length $\dfrac{7}{2}$, and so the perimeter of the star is $12\left(\dfrac{7}{2}\right) = 42$.

13. *Solution*

    In isosceles $\triangle DAB$, $\angle DAB = \angle DBA$

    $\qquad\qquad\qquad = x + 15$.

    Since $\angle ABC = 180°$, $\angle DBC = 180 - (x + 15)$

    $\qquad\qquad\qquad\qquad = 165 - x$.

    In $\triangle DBC$, $(x - 15) + x + (165 - x) = 180$

    $\qquad\qquad\qquad\qquad 150 + x = 180$

    $\qquad\qquad\qquad\qquad\quad x = 30$.

    The value of x is 30.

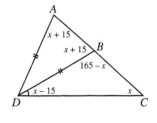

14. *Solution*

    Since chords equidistant from the centre of a circle
    are equal in length, the four shorter chords are the
    same length.

    Since radius OD is perpendicular to chord AC,

    $AB = BC$.

    In triangle OBC, $OB = 1$ and radius $OC = 2$.

    Using the Pythagorean Theorem,

    $$BC^2 + 1^2 = 2^2$$

    $$BC^2 = 3$$

    $$BC = \sqrt{3}.$$

    Hence chord AC has length $2\sqrt{3}$.

    Each diameter has length 4.

    Thus the sum of the lengths of the six chords is $8 + 8\sqrt{3}$.

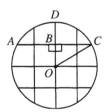

15. *Solution*

Extend TP to meet RS at Q.

Since $\angle WPT$ and $\angle QPU$ are opposite angles,

$\angle WPT = \angle QPU = x$.

In $\triangle PQS$, $2x + 26° + 90° = 180°$

$$2x = 64°$$

$$x = 32°.$$

Hence the value of x is $32°$.

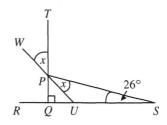

16. *Solution*

Let $\angle BDC = y$ and $\angle DBC = x$, with all angles measured in degrees.

Since $\triangle DBC$ is isosceles, $\angle DBC = \angle DCB = x$.

Since $\triangle CDA$ is isosceles, $\angle CDA = \angle DAC = 24 + y$.

In $\triangle DAC$, $24 + y + 24 + y + x = 180$

$$x + 2y + 48 = 180$$

$$x + 2y = 132. \qquad (1)$$

In $\triangle DBC$, $x + x + y = 180$

$$2x + y = 180. \qquad (2)$$

Multiply equation (1) by 2 and subtract equation (2) to give

$$3y = 84$$

$$y = 28.$$

Hence the measure of $\triangle BDC$ is $28°$.

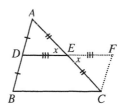

17. *Solution*

In order to prove lines parallel, we need a pair of equal corresponding or alternate angles.

This suggests some additional line segments be drawn in the diagram.

Extend DE to F so that $DE = EF$.

Join FC.

Since $\angle AED = \angle CEF$, $\triangle AED \equiv \triangle CEF$.

Thus $FC = AD$ and $\angle EAD = \angle ECF$.

Since $\angle EAD = \angle ECF$ and AC is a transversal, $AB \parallel CF$.

In quadrilateral $DBCF$, $DB = FC$ and $DB \parallel FC$.

Hence $DF = BC$ and $DF \parallel BC$.

Since $DE = \frac{1}{2}DF$, $DE = \frac{1}{2}BC$.

Thus the line which joins the mid-points of two sides of a triangle is parallel to the third side and equal to one-half its length.

18. *Solution*

Consider right-angled $\triangle ABC$ with $\angle ABC = 90°$
and D the mid-point of the hypotenuse AC.
Join BD and draw $DQ \perp AB$ and $DP \perp BC$.
Since $QD \parallel BC$, and AC is a transversal,
$\angle ADQ = \angle DCP$.
In triangles AQD and DPC,

$$\angle ADQ = \angle DCP$$
$$\angle AQD = \angle DPC = 90°$$
$$AD = DC$$

Hence $\triangle AQD \equiv \triangle DPC$.
Thus $QD = PC$.
Since $QDPB$ is a rectangle, $QD = BP = PC$.
In triangles DCP and DBP,

DP is common
$$\angle DPC = \angle DPB$$
$$PC = PB$$

Thus $\triangle DCP \equiv \triangle DBP$ and $DB = DC$.
Hence the mid-point of the hypotenuse of a right-
angled triangle is equidistant from all three vertices.

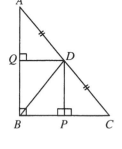

19. *Solution*

Extend AP to meet CB extended at R, and extend
AQ to meet BC extended at S.
Then $\triangle APC \equiv \triangle RPC$ because CP is common,
$\angle ACP = \angle RCP$, and $\angle APC = \angle RPC = 90°$.
Then P is the midpoint of AR.
By a similar method, Q is the midpoint of AS. The
line joining the midpoints of two sides of a triangle
is parallel to the third side.
Hence in $\triangle ARS$, PQ is parallel to RS (or BC).

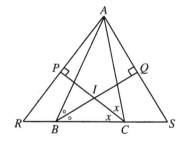

20. *Solution*

The given information suggests that line segments
ZW and ZV be drawn. Since ZW is a diameter,
angle WVZ is a right angle.
Since W is the midpoint of the hypotenuse of right
angled triangle XYZ, $YW = XW = ZW = 25$.
In triangle ZVW,

$$ZV^2 + 7^2 = 25^2$$
$$ZV^2 = 576$$
$$ZV = 24.$$

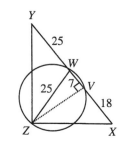

Since $WV = 7$, $VX = 25 - 7 = 18$.

In triangle ZXV,

$$ZX^2 = 18^2 + 24^2$$
$$= 324 + 576$$
$$= 900$$
$$ZX = 30.$$

Thus the length of XZ is 30.

21. *Solution*

The first step is to draw a diagram that incorporates all the given information. Since $CP = 2CB$, labelling M, the midpoint of CP, enbles us to illustrate this fact.

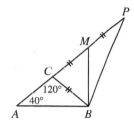

In $\triangle CAB$, $\angle CBA = 180° - 120° - 40°$
$$= 20°.$$

Since $\angle ACM$ is a straight angle, $\angle MCB = 60°$.

Thus, in isosceles $\triangle CBM$,

$$\angle CBM = \angle CMB = \frac{180° - 60°}{2} = 60°.$$

Hence $\triangle CBM$ is equilateral and so $MB = MP$.

Since $\angle CMP = 180°$, $\angle PMB = 120°$.

Thus, in isosceles $\triangle MBP$,

$$\angle MBP = \angle MPB = \frac{180° - 120°}{2} = 30°.$$

Hence, $\angle ABP = \angle ABC + \angle CBM + \angle MBP$
$$= 20° + 60° + 30°$$
$$= 110°.$$

22. *Solution*

Consider a polygon having n sides.

The sum of the interior and exterior angle at each vertex is $180°$.

Thus, the sum of the interior and exterior angles at all n vertices is $n \times 180°$.

Since the sum of the n interior angles is $n \times 180° - 360°$, the sum of the n exterior angles is $n \times 180° - (n \times 180° - 360°) = 360°$.

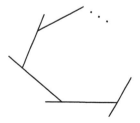

23. *Solution 1*

There are two approaches we could use; work with
the sum of the interior angles or use the fact that the
sum of the exterior angles is $360°$.
The latter approach often leads to a simpler
computation.

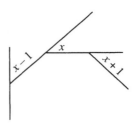

Since the measures of the interior angles are
consecutive integers, the measures of the exterior
angles are also consecutive integers.
In a situation when adding an odd number of
consecutive integers, the computation is simplified
by representing the middle number by the variable.
Let the measure of the middle exterior angle be x.
Then

$$(x-7)+(x-6)+(x-5)+\cdots+(x+6)+(x+7)=360$$
$$15x=360$$
$$x=24.$$

Hence the largest exterior angle is $24°+7°=31°$ and the smallest interior angle is
$180°-31°=149°$.

Note: Another variation would be to represent the largest exterior angle by x and
proceed to solve $x+(x-1)+(x-2)+\cdots+(x-14)=360$.

Solution 2

Let the measure of the middle interior angle be y.
Then $(y-7)+(y-6)+(y-5)+\cdots+(y+6)+(y+7)=180(15)-360$

$$15y=2340$$
$$y=156.$$

The smallest interior angle is $156°-7°=149°$.

24. *Solution*

Since the sum of the exterior angles of any polygon
is $360°$, it makes sense to consider the exterior
angles as the key to solving this problem.

Since exactly five interior angles are obtuse, then
exactly five exterior angles are acute. Each of the
remaining exterior angles has measure greater than
or equal to $90°$.
Since the five acute angles have a sum greater than
$0°$, (and the sum of all exterior angles is $360°$) then
the largest possible number of angles greater than
or equal to $90°$ is three.
Thus, the given polygon can have at most $3+5=8$
sides.

25. *Solution*

Since B is on a circle having centre A and A is on a circle having centre B, the two circles have equal radii.

Thus, $AC = AB = BE = BF$.

Let the measure of angle C, in degrees, be x.

Thus $\angle CAB = 180 - 2x$.

Since $\angle CAE = 180°$, $\angle EAB = 180 - (180 - 2x) = 2x$.

Since triangle BAE is isosceles, $\angle BEA = 2x$.

Since triangle BFE is isosceles, $\angle FEB = 78°$.

In triangle CFE, $\angle C + \angle F + \angle CEF = 180°$

$$x + 78° + 2x + 78° = 180°$$
$$3x = 24°$$
$$x = 8°.$$

Therefore $\angle C = 8°$.

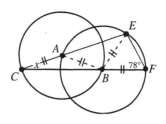

26. *Solution*

The first step is to draw a diagram that displays the given information.

Let O be the centre of the circle and let the radius of the circle be r.

Radii OA and OB are perpendicular to the tangents TA and TB, respectively.

Since $OA = OB$, $TAOB$ is a square.

Join OR and extend QR to meet OB at P.

$TQPR$ is a rectangle with $QP = TB = OA = r$.

Thus, $RP = r - 3$ and $OP = r - 6$.

In right angled triangle OPR,

$$OR^2 = RP^2 + OP^2$$
$$r^2 = (r-3)^2 + (r-6)^2$$
$$r^2 = r^2 - 6r + 9 + r^2 - 12r + 36$$
$$r^2 - 18r + 45 = 0$$
$$(r-15)(r-3) = 0$$
$$r = 15. \quad (r = 3 \text{ is inadmissible})$$

Thus the radius of the circle is 15.

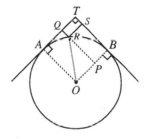

27.   *Solution*
       Since *MN* is a chord, drawing a line segment from
       the centre *O* perpendicular to *MN* would enable us
       to use the chord-radius properties of a circle.
       Draw *OT* perpendicular to chord *MN*.

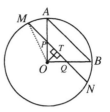

       The length of chord *MN* is $12 + \sqrt{56} = 12 + 2\sqrt{14}$.
       Thus the length of *MT* is $6 + \sqrt{14}$ and *PT* has
       length $6 + \sqrt{14} - 2\sqrt{14} = 6 - \sqrt{14}$.
       Since triangle *OAB* is a right-angled isosceles
       triangle, $\angle A = \angle B = 45°$.
       Since *MN* is parallel to *AB*, $\angle TPO = 45°$.

Thus triangle *OTP* is a right-angled isosceles triangle with $OT = PT = 6 - \sqrt{14}$.
In right-angled triangle *OTM*,

$$OM^2 = OT^2 + MT^2$$
$$= \left(6 - \sqrt{14}\right)^2 + \left(6 + \sqrt{14}\right)^2$$
$$= 36 - 12\sqrt{14} + 14 + 36 + 12\sqrt{14} + 14$$
$$= 100.$$
$$OM = 10.$$

Hence the radius of the given circle has length 10.

Chapter 5 *Solutions*

1. *Solution*
   Since the points are colinear, slope AD = slope BD.

   $$\frac{-y}{6} = \frac{2}{4}$$

   $$-y = \frac{1}{2} \times 6$$

   Thus, $y = -3$.

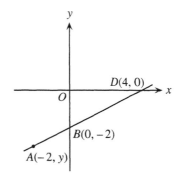

2. *Solution*
   Since Q is the midpoint of AC, point Q is $(3, 1)$.
   Since R is the midpoint of QC, point R is

   $$\left(\frac{3+6}{2}, \frac{1+0}{2}\right) = \left(\frac{9}{2}, \frac{1}{2}\right).$$

   The slope of OR is $\dfrac{\frac{1}{2} - 0}{\frac{9}{2} - 0} = \dfrac{1}{9}$.

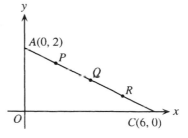

3. *Solution*
   Since both lines pass through $(-2, 1)$, the coordinates of the point must satisfy both equations.

   Thus, $-2t - 2 + k = 0$ (1)

   and $-6 + 1 - t = 0$.   (2)

   From (2) $t = -5$.

   Substitute in (1) to give $10 - 2 + k = 0$.

   Thus, the value for t is -5 and for k is -8.

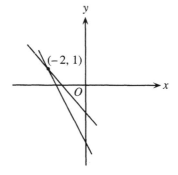

4. *Solution*

(a) The midpoint M is $\left(\dfrac{7-3}{2}, \dfrac{4-2}{2}\right) = (2, 1)$.

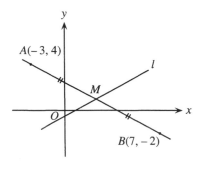

Slope $AB = \dfrac{-2-4}{7+3} = \dfrac{-3}{5}$.

Slope of line l is $\dfrac{-3}{5}+1 = \dfrac{2}{5}$.

Using $y - y_1 = m(x - x_1)$, the equation of AB is

$$y - 1 = \frac{2}{5}(x - 2)$$

or $\quad 2x - 5y + 1 = 0.$ (1)

(b) Since (k, m) is on the line l, it satisfies (1).

$$2k - 5m + 1 = 0$$
$$5m = 2k + 1.$$

Therefore $\qquad m = \dfrac{2k+1}{5}.$

5. *Solution*

Let point P be $(-5, k)$.

Since $AP = BP$, we use the distance formula to get

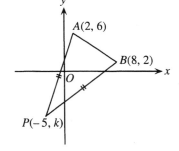

$$\sqrt{(-5-2)^2 + (k-6)^2} = \sqrt{(-5-8)^2 + (k-2)^2}.$$
$$49 + k^2 - 12k + 36 = 169 + k^2 - 4k + 4$$
$$-8k = 88$$
$$k = -11$$

Hence point P is $(-5, -11)$.

6. *Solution*

(a) If we use the property which states "if the slopes of the lines l_1 and l_2 are equal, then the lines are parallel", we should be able to solve the problem. First we must find points K, M, P, and Q.

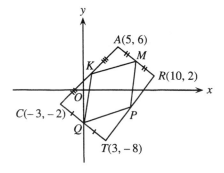

These points are $K(1, 2)$, $M(7.5, 4)$, $P(6.5, -3)$, and $Q(0, -5)$.

Thus, slope $KM = \dfrac{4-2}{7.5-1} = \dfrac{2}{6.5}$

and slope $QP = \dfrac{-3+5}{6.5-0} = \dfrac{2}{6.5}.$

Also, slope $QK = \dfrac{2+5}{1-10} = 7$

and slope $PM = \dfrac{4+3}{7.5-6.5} = 7$.

Since the slopes of opposite sides are equal, the opposite sides are parallel. This proves figure $KMPQ$ is a parallelogram.

(b) Draw any quadrilateral $CART$.
In a general problem such as this, you should avoid drawing a diagram with special characteristics such as equal sides or right angles.

Select a vertex, say C, as the origin and place the x-axis along CT.

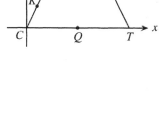

To avoid fractions, let the coordinates of A be $(2a, 2b)$, R be $(2c, 2d)$ and T be $(2g, 0)$.

The remainder of the proof is similar to part (a).

Your final result will have slope KM = slope OP

$$= \dfrac{d-0}{c+g-g}$$

$$= \dfrac{d}{c}.$$

7. *Solution*
Since $\angle PQR = 90°$, then the bisector of $\angle PQR$ makes an angle of $45°$ with the x-axis.

Thus, the slope of QW is 1.

The equation of QW is $y - 1 = 1(x - 3)$ or $x - y - 2 = 0$.

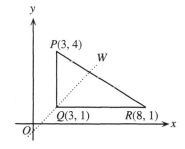

8.   *Solution*
     The sketch shows that point T is close to the
     line. To be certain we must conduct an
     algebraic test. Any one of the given tests is
     a complete solution.

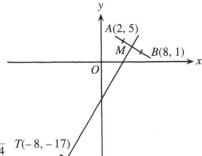

Test 1

Check the distances TA and TB to determine
if T is on the right bisector of AB.

$$TA = \sqrt{(2+8)^2 + (5+17)^2} = \sqrt{100+484} = \sqrt{584}$$

and

$$TB = \sqrt{(8+8)^2 + (1+18)^2} = \sqrt{256+361} = \sqrt{617}.$$

Since $TA \neq TB$, point T is not on the right bisector.

Test 2

The midpoint of AB is $M(5,3)$ and the slope of AB is $-\frac{2}{3}$.

The slope of TM is $\dfrac{1+17}{8+8} = \dfrac{9}{8}$.

Since $\left(-\dfrac{2}{3}\right)\left(\dfrac{9}{8}\right) = -\dfrac{3}{4} \neq -1$, TM is not perpendicular to AB.

Therefore T does not lie on the perpendicular bisector of AB.

Test 3

If two lines with slopes m_1 and m_2 are perpendicular, then $m_1 m_2 = -1$.

Since the slope of $AB = \dfrac{1-5}{8-2} = -\dfrac{2}{3}$, the slope of the right bisector of AB must be $\dfrac{3}{2}$.

The midpoint, M, of AB is $\left(\dfrac{2+8}{2}, \dfrac{5+1}{2}\right) = (5,3)$.

Hence, the equation of the right bisector of AB is $y-3 = \dfrac{3}{2}(x-5)$ or $3x-2y=9$.   (1)

Test point T in (1):   L.S. $= 3(-8)-2(-17) = 10$, and since this is not equal to the right side
of the equation, the point T is not on the right bisector.

9.   *Solution*

For $x + y = 6$, point C is $(6, 0)$.

For $4x - 7y + 20 = 0$, point B is $(-5, 0)$.

To find point A, solve the equations

$$4x - 7y = -20 \qquad (1)$$
$$x + y = 6 \qquad (2)$$

$4 \times (2)$ gives $\quad 4x + 4y = 24 \qquad (3)$

$(1) - (3)$ gives $\quad -11y = -44$

$$y = 4$$

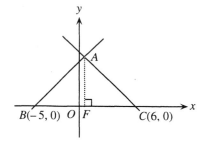

Thus, height $FA = 4$ and base $BC = 6 - (-5) = 11$.

Hence the area of triangle $ABC = \dfrac{1}{2}(11)(4) = 22$.

10. *Solution*

Let W be $(a, 0)$.

Since $RW = 13$, $\sqrt{(a - 7)^2 + 25} = 13$.

Square both sides: $a^2 - 14a + 49 + 25 = 169$

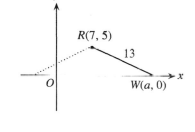

$$a^2 - 14a + 74 - 169 = 0$$
$$a^2 - 14a - 95 = 0$$
$$(a - 19)(a + 5) = 0.$$

Hence, $a = 19$ or $a = -5$.

It follows that there are two locations for point W, namely $(-5, 0)$ and $(19, 0)$.

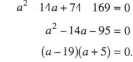

11. *Solution*

Let point A be $(1, 7)$.

Then slope $OA = 7$ and length

$OA = \sqrt{1 + 49} = \sqrt{50}$.

Since OB has slope one, let B be (b, b).

Thus, $OB = \sqrt{b^2 + b^2} = \sqrt{2b^2}$.

Since $OA = OB$, $\sqrt{2b^2} = \sqrt{50}$.

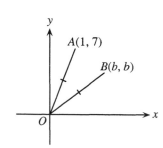

Square both sides to give $b^2 = 25$.

Therefore $b = \pm 5$, but we omit $b = -5$ since B is in the first quadrant.

The slope of $AB = \dfrac{5 - 7}{5 - 1} = -\dfrac{1}{2}$.

Note: This solution could begin by letting A be $(a, 7a)$. Eventually the a's will divide out. There is no loss of generality by setting $a = 1$, as shown.

12.   *Solution*
      Let A be $(a, 0)$.

      Slope $TA = \dfrac{-6}{a-13}$ and slope $RA = \dfrac{-9}{a+2}$.

      Since TA and RA are perpendicular, then

      $\left(\dfrac{-6}{a-13}\right)\left(\dfrac{-9}{a+2}\right) = -1$.

      $-(a-13)(a+2) = 54$

      $-a^2 + 11a + 26 = 54$

      $a^2 - 11a + 28 = 0$

      $(a-4)(a-7) = 0$.

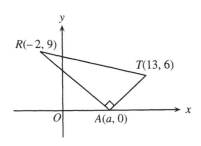

      Therefore $a = 4$ or $a = 7$.
      The two possible locations for A are $(4, 0)$ and $(7, 0)$.

13.   *Solution*
      Place the axes as shown and let the centre be
      $C(0, b)$.
      Since AC and DC are both radii,
      then $CA = DC$

      $11 - b = \sqrt{18 + b^2}$.

      Squaring, we get

      $121 - 22b + b^2 = 18 + b^2$

      $-22b = 203$

      $b = -\dfrac{203}{22} = -9.2$ (to one decimal place).

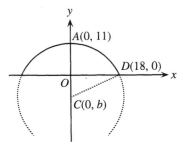

      The radius of the circular cross section is
      approximately $11 + 9.2 = 20.2$ m.

14.   *Solution*
      (a)   Let P be (x, y).
            The locus is a set of points, P, located so that
            $FP = QP$.
            Since PQ is perpendicular to $y = -3$, the
            coordinates of Q are $(x, -3)$.
            Since $FP = QP$,

            $\sqrt{x^2 + (y-3)^2} = \sqrt{(x-x)^2 + (y+3)^2}$.

            Square both sides to give

            $x^2 + y^2 - 6y + 9 = y^2 + 6y + 9$.

            Simplifying, we get $x^2 = 12y$ as the equation of the locus.

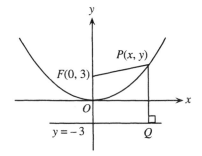

(b)　In the generalized solution the explanation is the same as in part (a).

The length formula gives $\sqrt{x^2+(y-p)^2}=\sqrt{(x-x)^2+(y+p)^2}$　or　$x^2=4py$.

This formula can be written as $y=ax^2$, where $a=\dfrac{1}{4p}$.

It is the general formula for any parabola with vertex the origin and symmetric about the y-axis.

15.　*Solution*

The path followed by the particle when it leaves the circle is a tangent at R.

Use the property that the tangent is perpendicular to the radius at R to find the slope of the tangent.

Since slope $OR=-\dfrac{3}{4}$, the slope of the tangent is $\dfrac{4}{3}$.

The equation of the straight line trajectory is

$y+6=\dfrac{4}{3}(x-8)$ or $4x-3y=50$.

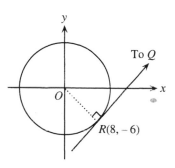

To determine if the particle collides with Q, test $Q(100,120)$ to see if it is on the line:

　　L.S. $=4(100)-3(120)=40$ and R.S. $=50\neq$ L.S.

Hence the particle does not collide with the object at point Q.

16.　*Solution 1*

Let the coordinates of town W be (a,b).

Since $LW=MW$, point W is on the right bisector of LM.

The midpoint of LM is $Q(30,20)$, and so the equation of WQ is $x=30$.　(1)

Thus, $a=30$ and W is $(30,b)$.

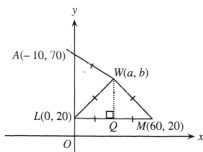

Since $AW=LW$,

$\sqrt{(30+10)^2+(b-70)^2}=\sqrt{30^2+(b-20)^2}$.　(2)

Square both sides

$1600+b^2-140b+4900=900+b^2-40b+400$

　　　　　$-100b=-5200$

　　　　　　$b=52$.

Who-ville is located at $(30,52)$.

Solution 2

An alternate approach, after finding W is $(30, b)$, is to find the slope of AL and the midpoint, P, of AL.

Then $(\text{slope } AL) \cdot (\text{slope } PW) = -1$ since AL and PW are perpendicular. This will give $b = 52$ as before.

17. *Solution*

    (a)   For clockwise order of vertices, the diagram is as shown.

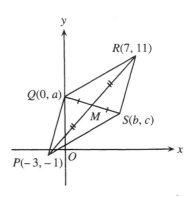

        The midpoint M of PR is

$$\left(\frac{7-3}{2}, \frac{11-1}{2}\right) = (2, 5).$$

        Since a geometric property of parallelograms is that the diagonals bisect each other, the midpoint of QS is also point M.

        Thus, $\left(\dfrac{0+b}{2}, \dfrac{a+c}{2}\right) = (2, 5).$

        This gives $b = 4$ and $a + c = 10$.

        Adding, we get $a + c + b = 14$.

    (b)   From part (a), we have $c = 10 - a$.

        Since a can take only the values 6, 7, 8, and 9, and since all corresponding values for c are integers, a total of four parallelograms are possible.

18. *Solution*

Place the axes as shown in the diagram.

Then point B is $(3, -6)$.

A parabola in this position has equation

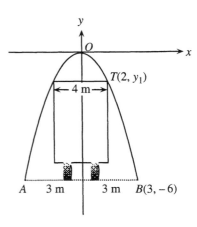

$$y = ax^2. \quad (1)$$

Point $B(3, -6)$ must satisfy (1).

Therefore $-6 = 9a$

$$a = -\frac{2}{3}.$$

The equation of the parabola is $y = -\dfrac{2}{3}x^2.$ (2)

Let the coordinates of the top right corner of the truck be $T(2, y_1)$.

If the top just touches the tunnel then $(2, y_1)$ satisfies (2)

$$y_1 = -\frac{2}{3}(4) = -\frac{8}{3}.$$

The maximum height of the truck is $6 - \dfrac{8}{3} = \dfrac{10}{3}$ m. In practical terms the truck height would have to be less than this.

19. *Solution 1*

Let the required point be $P(a, b)$.
Since P is on the line its coordinates must
satisfy the equation $3x - 2y + 37 = 0$.
Therefore $3a - 2b + 37 = 0$. (1)
We know $AP = BP$.

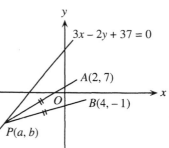

Hence, $\sqrt{(a-2)^2 + (b-7)^2} = \sqrt{(a-4)^2 + (b+1)^2}$.

Square to get

$a^2 - 4a + 4 + b^2 - 14b + 49 = a^2 - 8a + 16 + b^2 + 2b + 1$

$\qquad 4a - 16b + 36 = 0$

$\qquad\qquad a - 4b + 9 = 0$. (2)

To find the required point solve equations (1) and (2)
$3 \times$ (1) gives $3a - 12b + 27 = 0$ (3)
(1) – (3) gives $\qquad 10b + 10 = 0$

$\qquad\qquad\qquad b = -1$

Substitute in (2) and $\qquad a = -13$.
Point $P(-13, -1)$ is on the line and also is equidistant from A to B.

Solution 2
Find the slope of AB and use it to get the slope and equation of the right bisector of AB.
Solve this equation with $3x - 2y + 37 = 0$.

20. *Solution*
To find point A, we must first find the equation of
AC and then solve the new equation with
$3x - 4y + 2 = 0$ (1)

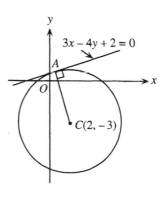

Since the slope of (1) is $\frac{3}{4}$, the slope of AC is $-\frac{4}{3}$.

The equation of AC is $y + 3 = -\frac{3}{4}(x - 2)$

$\qquad$ or $\qquad\qquad 4x + 3y = -1$. (2)
$4 \times$ (2) gives $\qquad 16x + 12y = -4$ (3)
$3 \times$ (1) gives $\qquad 9x - 12y = -6$ (4)
(3) + (4) gives $\qquad\qquad 25x = -10$

$\qquad\qquad\qquad\qquad x = -\frac{2}{5}$.

Substitute in (1) to get $y = \frac{1}{5}$ and point A is $\left(-\frac{2}{5}, \frac{1}{5}\right)$.

Then the radius $AC = \sqrt{\left(2 + \frac{2}{5}\right)^2 + \left(-3 - \frac{1}{5}\right)^2} = \sqrt{\frac{144}{25} + \frac{256}{25}} = 4$.

The equation of the circle is $(x - 2)^2 + (y + 3)^2 = 16$.

21. *Solution*

  (a) This locus is not easy to visualize. All we can
       do at this point is sketch the information that
       has been given.

       The definition of the locus, as given in the
       problem, is that P is located so that

       Area $\triangle PUB = (QP)^2.$ $\qquad$ (1)

       Let the coordinates of P be (x, y).

       To translate (1) into algebra we need point Q
       and the area of $\triangle PUB$.

       Since PQ is perpendicular to the y-axis, $QP = x$.

       Area $\triangle PUB = \dfrac{1}{2}(\text{base } UB)(\text{height})$

       $\qquad = \dfrac{1}{2}(2)(y)$

       $\qquad = y.$

       Equation (1) becomes $y = x^2$, and this is the equation of the locus.

  (b) The equation $y = x^2$ is of the form $y = ax^2$ and, much to our surprise, this locus is a
       parabola with vertex at the origin and opening upward. Notice that locus problems can
       begin with unusual definitions and end up producing well known curves.

22. *Solution 1*

  (a) Since there is no apparent right angle
       in $\triangle BAR$, construct $BK, RQ,$ and AN
       perpendicular to the x-axis. This
       creates three trapezoids which are
       used as follows:

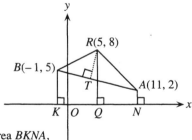

       Area $\triangle BAR$ = area $BKQR$ + area $RQNA$ − area $BKNA$,
       where the vertical lengths we need are $KB = 5$,
       $QR = 8$, $NA = 2$, and the horizontal lengths are
       $KQ = 6$, $QN = 6$ and $KN = 12$.

       Thus, area $\triangle BAR = \dfrac{1}{2}\big[(KB+QR)(KQ)+(QR+NA)(QN)-(KB+NA)(KN)\big]$

       $\qquad = \dfrac{1}{2}\big[(5+8)(6)+(8+2)(6)-(5+2)(12)\big]$

       $\qquad = \dfrac{1}{2}[78+60-84]$

       $\qquad = 27.$

Solution 2

If you construct $RT \perp BA$, then the area is given by $\frac{1}{2}(BA)(TR)$. Unfortunately point

T works out to be $\left(\frac{419}{109}, \frac{452}{109}\right)$, and the arithmetic involved in finding TR is rather

tedious.

Solution

(b) When you calculate the horizontal
     lengths find all the directed distances
     in the positive direction.
     For example $KQ = x_3 - x_1$. The
     explanation is the same as in part (a),
     but the algebra is rather lengthy. A
     mnemonic that will help you to
     quickly calculate the area is to list the
     ordered pairs in a column and repeat
     the first ordered pair.

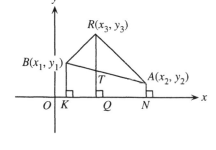

Then the area of

$$\triangle ABC - \frac{1}{2}\left|(\text{sum of the downward products}) - (\text{sum of the upward products})\right|$$

$$= \frac{1}{2}\left|(x_1y_2 + x_2y_3 + x_3y_1) - (x_1y_3 + x_3y_2 + x_2y_1)\right|.$$

The use of absolute value bars will ensure that the area is a positive number.
Try this pattern to calculate the area of the triangle in part (a).
Another way to calculate the area of a triangle is to use Heron's formula. It is left as
a project for you to find this formula and learn how to apply it.

23. *Solution*
     If we draw perpendiculars to the x-axis, it will not
     be a simple combination of trapezoids that will give
     the area. To simplify the problem, slide the triangle
     4 units up until point A is on the x-axis.
     The new triangle will have vertices $B_1(-3, 3)$,
     $C_1(4, 9)$ and $A_1(7, 0)$ and it will have the same
     dimensions as $\triangle ABC$.
     To find the area, construct B_1K and C_1Q
     perpendicular to the x-axis.

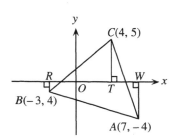

Area $\triangle A_1 B_1 C_1$ = Area trapezoid $B_1 KQC_1$ + area $\triangle C_1 QA_1$ − area $\triangle B_1 KA_1$

$$= \frac{1}{2}\big[(KB_1 + QC_1)(KQ) + (QA_1)(QC_1) - (KA_1)(KB)\big]$$

$$= \frac{1}{2}\big[(3+9)(7) + (3)(9) - (10)(3)\big]$$

$$= \frac{1}{2}[84 + 27 - 30]$$

$$= \frac{1}{2}[81]$$

$$= 40.5$$

$$= \text{area } \triangle ABC.$$

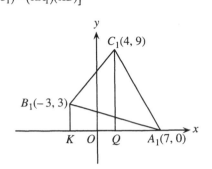

24. *Solution*

Let the centre of the circle be at the origin and
let the radius be r.

Let the coordinates of P be (x, y).

Then the equation of the circle is $x^2 + y^2 = r^2$. (1)

The coordinates of A and B are $(-r, 0)$ and
$(r, 0)$, respectively.

To show that $\angle APB$ is a right angle we must
prove that $(\text{slope } AP) \cdot (\text{slope } BP) = -1$.

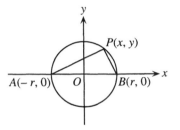

$$(\text{slope } AP) \cdot (\text{slope } BP) = \left(\frac{y}{x+r}\right)\left(\frac{y}{x-r}\right)$$

$$= \frac{y^2}{x^2 - r^2}$$

$$= \frac{y^2}{-y^2} \qquad \left(x^2 - r^2 = -y^2 \text{ from (1)}\right)$$

$$= -1.$$

Therefore AP is perpendicular to BP and angle APB is a right angle.

25. *Solution 1*

Let the coordinates of Q be (a, b).

Draw AW, WQ, QR, and RB parallel to the axes as shown.

The coordinates of R are $(10, b)$ and the coordinates of W are $(a, -4)$.

Triangle BQR is similar to triangle QAW since their corresponding angles are equal.

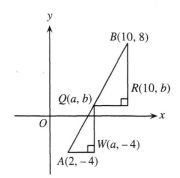

Therefore $\dfrac{AW}{QR} = \dfrac{AQ}{QB}$

$$\frac{a-2}{10-a} = \frac{3}{5}$$

$$5a - 10 = 30 - 3a$$

$$8a = 40$$

$$a = 5.$$

Similarly, $\dfrac{WQ}{RB} = \dfrac{AQ}{QB}$

$$\frac{b+4}{8-b} = \frac{3}{5}$$

$$5b + 20 = 24 - 3b$$

$$8b = 4$$

$$b = \frac{1}{2}.$$

The point Q has coordinates $\left(5, \dfrac{1}{2}\right)$.

Solution 2

A tempting approach is to use the ratio of lengths $AQ : AB = 3 : 8$.

The length formula gives the equation $8\sqrt{(a-2)^2 + (b+4)^2} = 3\sqrt{64 + 144}$. (1)

The second equation is found by substituting (a, b) into the equation of AB.

This gives the equation $3a - 2b = 14$. (2)

The algebra involved in solving equations (1) and (2) is much more difficult than the algebra in solution (1). The final result is the same.

Chapter 6   *Solutions*

1.   *Solution*

Since $4000 = 2^5 \times 5^2$, any squares that divide 4000 are composed of 2's and 5's.

The squares that can be created from five 2's and two 5's are $2^2, 2^4, 5^2, 2^2 \times 5^2$, and $2^4 \times 5^2$. There are five perfect squares that divide 4000.

2.   *Solution*

It is easier to list the perfect squares between 10 and 200 and check whether the number following is a prime, than to list the primes between 10 and 200 and check whether the preceding number is a perfect square.

If we list all of the perfect squares between 10 and 200, the only ones which are immediately followed by prime numbers are 16, 36, 100, and 196.

3.   *Solution 1*

All four digit codes in which zeroes are never adjacent are 1111, 1110, 1101, 1011, 0111, 0110, 0101, 1010.

Thus there are eight such codes.

Solution 2

If there are never any adjacent zeros, then the code can consist of all 1's, or three 1's and one 0, or two 1's and two 0's.

There is only one code with four 1's, namely 1111.

If the code has three 1's and one 0, there are four positions for the 0 with the remaining positions all 1's, so there are four such codes.

If the code has two 0's and two 1's, the 0's must be in positions 1 and 3 (giving 0101), or they must be in positions 2 and 4 (giving 1010), or they must be in positions 1 and 4 (giving 0110). This gives three additional codes.

There are eight such codes altogether.

Comment

The second solution is longer, but makes extension of the problem easier. You might wish to repeat this question for five-digit (13 codes possible) or six-digit codes.

We leave it to you to determine the number of codes in the last case.

4.   *Solution*

Every winning number is of the form $p86q$, where p and q are digits, with $p = 1, 2, ..., 9$ and $q = 0, 1, 2, ..., 9$.

If the number is divisible by 15, then it is divisible by both 5 and 3.

If the number is divisible by 5, then its units digit is either a zero of a five.

Hence winning numbers are of the form $p860$ or $p865$.

If the number is divisible by 3, then the sum of its digits is also divisible by 3.

If the units digit is 0, the only possibilities for the number are 1860, 4860, and 7860.

If the units digit is 5, the only possibilities for the number are 2865, 5865, and 8865.

Therefore there are six winning tickets.

5. *Solution*

Since q appears in each term, set $q = 13$ to maximize the result. Now we maximize the remainder by setting $p = 11$, because it is multiplied by 3, then $r = 5$, because it is multiplied by 2, and then $s = 2$.

The largest possible value of $3pq + 2qr + qs$ is $13(3 \times 11 + 2 \times 5 + 2) = 13(45) = 585$.

6. *Solution*

The number 24 can be the sum of three digits only as $9 + 9 + 6$, $9 + 8 + 7$, or $8 + 8 + 8$.

From 9, 9, 6, three integers can be formed, since the 6 can be the first, or second, or third digit, and the others are then fixed.

From 7, 8, 9, six integers can be formed, since there are three positions for placing 7 and for each of these there are two positions for the 8, with the 9 then fixed.

From 8, 8, 8, only one integer can be formed.

There are 10 positive three-digit numbers such that the sum of the three digits is 24.

7. *Solution*

Let the two digit number be $10a + b$.

Then the number with digits reversed is $10b + a$. (Note that neither a nor b can be 0).

Then, $10a + b - 54 = 10b + a$

$$9a - 9b = 54$$

$$a - b = 6.$$

The solutions to this equation are $(a, b) = (7, 1), (8, 2), (9, 3)$.

The numbers are 71, 82, 93.

8. *Solution* .

Each pile has 10 cards in it.

The smallest possible sum of 10 cards is $1 + 2 + 3 + \ldots + 10 = 55$.

The largest possible sum is $40 + 39 + 38 + \ldots + 31 = 355$.

Since every sum between 55 and 355 can be obtained, the number of possible sums is $355 - 54$ or 301.

9. *Solution*

(a) By factoring, $630 = 63 \times 10 = 2 \times 3^2 \times 5 \times 7$.

The three integers must be 2, 15, 21.

(b) (i) In order to make the sum of the three integers as large as possible, make one of the integers as large as possible.

Hence, using 2, 3, and 105, we obtain the sum 110.

(ii) In order to make the sum as small as possible, make the three numbers as close to being equal as possible.

Hence, using 7, 9, and 10, we obtain the sum 26.

10. *Solution*

If the number is divisible by 36, it must be divisible by both 4 and 9.

If the number is divisible by 4, the last two digits must form a two-digit number divisible by 4. Then U must be 2 or 6, because 72 and 76 are the only possible choices for the last two digits.

If the number is divisible by 9, the sum of the digits must be a multiple of 9.

The sum of the digits is $22 + T + U$.

If $U = 2$, then $T = 3$, to give a digit sum of 27.

If $U = 6$, then $T = 8$, to give a digit sum of 36.

The possible values for (T, U) are $(3, 2)$ and $(8, 6)$.

11. *Solution*

If N is divisible by 66, it is divisible by 2, 3, and 11.

If N is divisible by 2, then T is even; that is, $T = 0, 2, 4, 6, 8$.

If N is divisible by 3, then $18 + T$ is a multiple of 3.

Hence, $T = 0, 3, 6,$ or 9.

These two conditions are possible only if $T = 0$ or 6.

If N is divisible by 11, then $6 + 1 + T = 8 + 3$

$$7 + T = 11$$
$$T = 4.$$

This is impossible.

There is no value for T that makes N divisible by 66.

12. *Solution*

Let the two-digit integer be of the form ab, where a and b are single digits.

Then the number can be written $10a + b$ and if the digits are reversed we have $10b + a$.

We are looking for values of a and b such that

$$10a + b + 11 = 10b + a$$
$$9a = 9b - 11$$
$$a = \frac{9b - 11}{9}$$
$$= b - \frac{11}{9}.$$

But this equation has no solutions where a and b are single digits.

Thus there are no two-digit integers that are increased by 11 when the order of the digits is reversed.

13. *Solution*

(a) If a number is to be divisible by 9, then the sum of its digits must also be divisible by 9.

Since we are considering ten-digit positive integers, consisting of ones and zeros, the only way for the sum of the digits to be divisible by 9 is if nine of the digits are ones and the tenth digit is zero.

Since the zero cannot occur in the leading position, there are nine possible positions in which the zero can be placed.

Hence there are nine possible numbers divisible by 9.

(b) From part (a) there must be 9 ones and 2 zeros.

Again, the first digit must be one, so there are 10 positions in which to place 8 ones and 2 zeros.

Since the number of zeros is smaller, it is simpler to position them, with all remaining positions receiving a one.

There are 10 choices for the first zero, and for each of these there are 9 choices for the second, so it appears that there are 90 ways to position for the 2 zeros. However, each possible choice appears twice. (Why is this so?)

Hence there are 45 positionings for the zeros, and 45 possible eleven-digit numbers divisible by 9.

14. *Solution*

The smallest sum is $1+0+0=1$.

The largest sum is $9+9+9=27$.

Therefore there are 27 possible sums.

Thus, if 28 cards are drawn, one of the sums will be repeated.

15. *Solution*

If p is a prime, its only positive divisors are 1 and p.

The positive divisors of 15 are 1, 3, 5, and 15.

The positive divisors of $15p$ are all combinations of one of each of the divisors of p and 15, or 1, 3, 5, 15, p, $3p$, $5p$, and $15p$.

The sum of these divisors is $1+3+5+15+p+3p+5p+15p = 24(1+p)$.

16. *Solution*

Since $a+b=c$, then $a=c-b$.

All primes other than 2 are odd and since $a < b < c$, then b and c must be odd primes. Thus, $a=2$ because the difference between odd numbers is even.

It follows that b and c differ by 2, so we are looking for pairs of primes that differ by 2 (called twin primes) and are less than 40. These are $(3, 5), (5, 7), (11, 13), (17, 19)$, and $(29, 31)$.

There are five sets: $(2, 3, 5), (2, 5, 7), (2, 11, 13), (2, 17, 19)$, and $(2, 29, 31)$.

17. *Solution*

Note: Recall that in a perfect square every prime factor occurs an even number of times.

The prime factorization of 392 is $2^3 \cdot 7^2$.

If the perfect square is divisible by 392, then it must contain $2^4 \cdot 7^2 = 784$, and it must contain some other factor that is also a square, say k^2.

Then, $784k^2 \geq 20\,000$

$$k^2 \geq 25.51.$$

The smallest square that is greater than 25 is 36.

The smallest perfect square greater than 20 000 and divisible by 392 is

$$784 \times 36 = 28\,224 = 168^2.$$

18. *Solution*

Let $x = 0.a7a7a7a7\ldots$.

Then $100x = a7.a7a7a7\ldots$ and, subtracting the first equation from the second, we get

$99x = a7$, or $x = \frac{a7}{99}$.

This is the fractional representation for the given repeating decimal, where a is a single digit. Since there are only ten possible values for a, we consider the ten possible values for the fraction x, checking that they are in reduced form. For example, when $a = 0$, $x = \frac{7}{99}$, which is already in reduced form.

The following list represents all other possible values of x:

$$\frac{17}{99}, \frac{27}{99} = \frac{3}{11}, \frac{37}{99}, \frac{47}{99}, \frac{57}{99} = \frac{19}{33}, \frac{67}{99}, \frac{77}{99}, \frac{87}{99} = \frac{29}{33}.$$

Thus, the smallest possible value for the sum of the numerator and denominator is $3 + 11 = 14$, and this occurs when $a = 2$.

19. *Solution*

$$m^3 - 4m = m\left(m^2 - 4\right) = m(m-2)(m+2)$$

Hence $m^3 - 4m$ is the product of three integers differing by 2 successively.

Since m is even, each of the integers is even and since $(m-2)$ and m are consecutive even integers, one of them is divisible by 4.

Therefore $(m-2)m(m+2)$ is divisible by $2 \times 4 \times 2$ or 16.

Since $(m-2)$, m, and $(m+2)$ are three consecutive even integers, one of them is divisible by 3.

Hence, $(m-2)(m)(m+2)$ is divisible by 3×16 or 48.

20. *Solution*

(a)   If a number is divisible by 6, it is divisible by both 2 and 3.

Since the palindrome must be divisible by 2, the last digit will be even.

Hence, the first digit will also be even, and the largest possible first digit is 8.

The largest possible second digit is 9, which would cause the fourth digit to be 9.

In order to determine the middle digit of the palindrome, we use the fact that if a number is divisible by 3, the sum of its digits is also divisible by 3.

Let a represent the middle digit of the palindrome.

Then $8 + 9 + a + 9 + 8 = 34 + a$ must be divisible by 3.

The largest possible value for a for which this is true is 8, and this the largest five-digit palindrome divisible by 6 is 89 898.

(b)   If a number is divisible by 12, it is divisible by both 4 and 3.

A number is divisible by 4 if its last two digits form a two-digit number divisible by 4.

[Why is this? Every number of more than two digits can be written as the sum of a number that is a multiple of 100 plus a two-digit number formed by its last two digits. For example, $1748 = 1700 + 48$. Can you see why the statement is true?]

The palindrome must have as its last two digits a two-digit number divisible by 4, and since the last digit is also the first in a palindrome, we use 88 as the last two, and the first two digits.

Then the number is $88a88$, and for divisibility by 3 the sum of the digits, $32 + a$, is divisible by 3.

Hence, $a = 1$, 4, or 7, and 7 gives the largest number.

Thus the palindrome is 88 788.

21. *Solution*

From the given conditions we can write $(a+b) + (a-b) + ab + \frac{a}{b} = 36$.

Hence, $2ab + ab^2 + a = 36b$, since $b \neq 0$

$$a = \frac{36b}{(b+1)^2}.$$

Now b and $(b+1)$ are relatively prime, so if a is an integer, $(b+1)^2$ must divide 36. Since $b \geq 1$ and $b+1 \leq 6$, the only allowable values are $b = 1$, which gives $a = 9$, and $b = 2$, which gives $a = 8$.

The pairs are $(9, 1)$ and $(8, 2)$.

[*Note*: Two numbers are relatively prime if they have no common divisor other than 1.]

22. *Solution*

(a)   You might want to try possibilities, using your calculator. You will quickly determine that 75 and 77 are the numbers you are looking for.

Alternatively, by listing the multiples of 5 and checking the number greater by 2, we obtain

25	30	35	40	45	50	55	60	65	70	75
27	32	37	42	47	52	57	62	67	72	77

Note that 40 and 42 satisfy the conditions of divisibility, but are not odd integers.

(b)   Let the numbers be m and $m+2$. Since m is a multiple of 5, we write $m = 5p$, and since $m+2$ is a multiple of 7, we write $m+2 = 7q$, with p and q integers.

Then $7q - 5p = 2$.

The simplest integer solution for this is $q = p = 1$.

The next solution is $q = 6$, $p = 8$, and this is followed by $q = 11$, $p = 15$.

In fact, a completely general solution is $q = 1 + 5t$, $p = 1 + 7t$, where t is an integer. (Can you justify this?)

Hence, $m = 5 + 35t$ and $m + 2 = 7 + 35t$, and you can see that if t is an odd integer we obtain even numbers satisfying the divisibility conditions, while if t is odd we obtain odd numbers.

23. *Solution*

The fractions $\frac{a}{b}$, where a and b are positive integers, $a+b=333$ and $\frac{a}{b}<1$, are elements of

$$\left\{\frac{1}{332}, \frac{2}{331}, \frac{3}{330}, \cdots, \frac{165}{168}, \frac{166}{167}\right\}.$$

This set has 166 elements.

Fractions of this type reduce only if a and $333-a$ have a common factor.

Since $333=3^2(37)$, the fractions reduce only if a is an integer multiple of 3 or 37.

Fractions of this type where a is an integer multiple of 3 are elements of $\left\{\frac{3}{330}, \frac{6}{327}, \cdots, \frac{165}{168}\right\}.$

This set has 55 elements.

Fractions of this type where a is an integer multiple of 37 are elements of $\left\{\frac{37}{8(37)}, \cdots, \frac{4(37)}{5(37)}\right\}.$

This set has 4 elements, but one was counted above, namely, the element $\frac{3(37)}{6(37)}.$

Therefore the number of fractions of the required form which will reduce is $55+3=58$, and the number of fractions which will not reduce is $166-58=108.$

24. *Solution*

$$x^2+6x+y^2=4$$
$$\left(x^2+6x+9\right)+y^2=4+9$$
$$(x+3)^2+y^2=13$$
$$(x+3)^2=13-y^2.$$

Since $13-y^2$ must be a perfect square, $y=\pm2, \pm3.$

If $y=\pm2, (x+3)^2=9.$
$$x+3=\pm3$$
$$x=0 \text{ or } -6.$$

If $y=\pm3, (x+3)^2=4$
$$x+3=\pm2$$
$$x=-1 \text{ or } -5.$$

Thus, there are 8 ordered pairs of integers (x, y) which satisfy the equation, namely $(0, 2), (0, -2), (-6, 2), (-6, -2), (-1, 3), (-1, -3), (-5, 3), (-5, -3).$

25. *Solution*

(a) The number of elements in the first 20 sets is $1+2+3+\cdots+20=\frac{20\times21}{2}=210.$

The odd integers are given by $2n-1, n=1, 2, 3, \cdots.$

Hence the last element in the 20th set is $2(210)-1=419.$

The 21 elements in the 21st set are $\{421, 423, \cdots, 459, 461\}.$

The sum of these elements is $421+423+\cdots+459+461$

$$=21\left(\frac{421+461}{2}\right)$$

$$=9261.$$

(b) *Solution 1*

The number of elements in the first $(n-1)$ sets is $1+2+3+\cdots+(n-1)=\dfrac{(n-1)n}{2}$.

The last element in the $(n-1)$th set is $2\left[\dfrac{(n-1)n}{2}\right]-1=n^2-n-1$.

Then the n elements in the nth set are $\left\{n^2-n+1, n^2-n+3, n^2-n+5, \ldots, n^2+n-1\right\}$.

Note: $n^2+n-1=n^2-n-1+2n$.

The sum of these elements is

$$\left(n^2-n+1\right)+\left(n^2-n+3\right)+\left(n^2-n+5\right)+\cdots+\left(n^2+n-1\right)$$

$$=\left(\frac{2n^2}{2}\right)n$$

$$=n^3.$$

Solution 2

The number of elements in the first $(n-1)$ sets is $1+2+3+\cdots+(n-1)=\dfrac{(n-1)n}{2}$.

The last element in the $(n-1)$th set is $2\left[\dfrac{(n-1)n}{2}\right]-1=n^2-n-1$.

The sum of all elements in the first $(n-1)$ sets is

$$1+3+5+\cdots+\left(n^2-n-1\right)=\frac{n^2-n}{2}\cdot\frac{(n-1)n}{2}$$

$$=\frac{n^2(n-1)^2}{4}.$$

The number of elements in the first n sets is $\dfrac{(n-1)n}{2}+n=\dfrac{n^2+n}{2}$.

The last element in the nth set is $2\left(\dfrac{n^2+n}{2}\right)-1=n^2+n-1$.

The sum of all elements in the first n sets is

$$1+3+5+\cdots+\left(n^2+n-1\right)=\frac{n^2+n}{2}\cdot\frac{n^2+n}{2}$$

$$=\frac{n^2(n+1)^2}{4}.$$

Then the sum of all elements in the nth set is

$$\frac{n^2(n+1)^2}{4}-\frac{n^2(n-1)^2}{4}=\frac{n^2}{4}\left[(n+1)^2-(n-1)^2\right]$$

$$=n^3.$$

Note the advantage of doing the problem in general. We could now give the sum of the elements in any set immediately. It seems harder to do the general version of a problem, but it frequently pays greater dividends to do so.

26. *Solution 1*

The remainder when any integer, with two or more digits, is divided by 100 is the number formed by the last two digits of the integer.

Instead of working with powers of 1995, we need only consider the last few digits of powers of 95.

$$95^2 = 9025$$
$$95^3 = 857375$$
$$95^4 = 81450625$$
$$95^5 = ...9375$$
$$95^6 = ...625$$

It appears that even powers of 1995 end in 25 and odd powers of 1995 end in 75.

Thus, 1995^{1993} leaves remainder 75 when divided by 100.

These conjectures can be proved by considering the binomial expansion of $(100 - 5)^n$, where n may be either an even or an odd positive integer.

Solution 2 (Using Congruences)

$$1995 \equiv 95 \pmod{100}$$

Therefore, $1995^n \equiv 95^n \pmod{100}$

$$\equiv (-5)^n \pmod{100}.$$

If n is even, $(-5)^n \equiv 25 \pmod{100}$.

If n is odd, $(-5)^n \equiv -25 \pmod{100}$

$$\equiv 75 \pmod{100}.$$

Hence, $1995^{1993} \equiv 75 \pmod{100}$.

When 1995^{1993} is divided by 100, the remainder is 75.

27. *Solution*

The number 49 in base p is $4p + 9$, where $p > 9$.

Similarly, 94 in base q is $9q + 4$, where $q > 9$.

$$4p + 9 = 9q + 4$$
$$9q = 4p + 5$$
$$q = \frac{4p + 5}{9}.$$

Since q must be an integer, then $4p + 5$ must be a multiple of 9.

When $p = 1$ we have $q = 1$, but this is inadmissible, since we require $p > 9$ and $q > 9$.
Similarly, the cases $(p, q) = (10, 5)$ and $(p, q) = (19, 9)$ are inadmissible.
The next possible solution is $(p, q) = (28, 13)$.
Therefore the least possible value of the number is $4 \times 28 + 9 = 121$.
Question: Can you list the next three possible values for the number and then give a general expression for all numbers that satisfy this condition?

28. *Solution*
Let the two digit number be $10a + b$.
Then $888(10a + b) = 1752(10b + a)$

$$8880a + 888b = 17\,520b + 1752a$$
$$7128a = 16\,632b.$$

Since the sum of the digits of each coefficient is 18, we can divide each side by 9 to give $792a = 1848b$.
Since the coefficients add to 18 on the left side and 21 on the right side, we can divide by 3 to give $264a = 616b$.
Since the last two digits of each coefficient are a multiple of 4, divide by 4 to obtain $66a = 154b$.
We can now divide by 11 and also by 2 to obtain the final simplified equation $3a = 7b$.
The only digits that satisfy this equation are $a = 7, b = 3$.
The number is 73.

29. *Solution*
There are 6 possible positions for placing the 2.
For any one of the positionings of the 2, there are 5 positions for placing the 3.
Hence, there are 6×5 ways to position the 2 and 3.
There are now 4 places in which to put the two 7's.
If the first 7 goes in the first empty position, there are three possible placings of the second 7.
If the first 7 goes in the second empty position, there are two possible placings of the second 7.
If the first 7 goes in the third empty position, there is only one placing for the second 7.
Hence, for each of the 6×5 placings of 2 and 3, there are 6 placings of the two 7's.
This leaves only one way of placing the 8's.
There are, then, $6 \times 5 \times 6 = 180$ possible numbers.

30. *Solution*

The number *strst* can be expressed as

$$10^4 s + 10^3 t + 10^2 r + 10 s + t = 10^3(80s + t) + 10^2 r + (10s + t)$$

$$= (10s + t)(10^3 + 1) + 10^2 r$$

$$= (10s + t)(1001), \quad \text{since } r = 0.$$

Now $1001 = 11 \times 91$ (remember the test for divisibility by 11)

$$= 11 \times 7 \times 13.$$

This gives three of the five primes, so $10s + t$ must be the two-digit product of two primes. Starting with 3, the smallest odd prime, we can use it with any one of 5, 7, 11, 13, 17, 19, 23, 29, 31 to obtain a two-digit number, so there are 9 such numbers having 3 as the smallest prime.

Starting with 5 as the smallest prime, we can use it with 5, 7, 11, 13, 17, 19 to obtain a two-digit number, so there are 6 such numbers having 5 as the smallest prime.

Starting with 7 as the smallest prime, we can use it with 7, 11, 13 to obtain a two-digit number, so there are 3 such numbers having 7 as the smallest prime.

There are no further possibilities; hence there are 18 numbers satisfying the conditions.

Question: Are you satisfied that all 18 numbers are different?

Chapter 7   Solutions

1. *Solution*
    Since the centre circle is connected to each of the
    others, it must have its own colour.
    The six circles around the outside can be coloured
    using two colours and alternating them.
    Thus at least three colours are required to properly
    colour the diagram.

    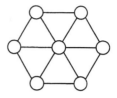

2. *Solution*
    If we start with 2, the 100th positive integers is 101. But there are 9 perfect squares between
    2 and 101 and so Barbie must extend her list by 9.
    Thus the 100th number of her list is $101 + 9 = 110$.

3. *Solution*
    All paths from Q to S must pass through R and the
    longest path from Q to R is QPR with length 2.
    The longest path from R to S is RTS, also with
    length 2.
    Combining these paths into the path $QPRTS$ gives the
    longest path from Q to S and it has length 4.

    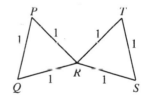

4. *Solution*
    Since the average is 69, the five integers sum to $5 \times 69 = 345$.
    Since the median is 83 and the mode is 85, there are two 85's and the two unknown integers
    are both less than 83.
    Their sum is $345 - (83 + 2(85)) = 92$.
    Since the range is 70 and the largest of the integers is 85, the smallest is $85 - 70 = 15$.
    Thus the second smallest of the five integers is $92 - 15 = 77$.

5. *Solution*
    Since the three sides of the triangle are the same
    length,
    $$7a - 3 = 5a + 15$$
    $$2a = 18$$
    $$a = 9.$$
    Thus $7a - 3 = 5a + 15 = 60$.
    Therefore $4x = 60$ and so $x = 15$ is the only possible
    value of x.

    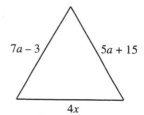

6.   *Solution*
     To achieve the largest sum, we need to make the individual numbers as large as possible. This
     is accomplished by using the largest digits in the hundred's place, then in the ten's place in
     the numbers.
     Thus we use the 6 and one 5 in the hundreds place of the three digit numbers.
     The other 5 and the two 4's are used in the ten's places, and the 3, 2, and 1 are used in the
     units places.
     The numbers could be 653, 542, and 41 and their sum is 1236.
     What other numbers will produce the same maximum sum of 1236?

7.   *Solution*
     Since the sum of the entries in the first row is
     $15+1+11=27$, the sums of the entries in every
     row, column, and diagonal must be 27.
     Hence the middle entry in the middle column must
     be 9 and the last entry in the bottom row must be 3.
     Thus $N=27-11-3=13$.

15	1	11
		N
	17	

8.   *Solution*
     There are eight 1×1 squares, five 2×2 squares,
     three 3×3 squares, and one 4×4 square.
     This gives a total of 17 squares of all sizes.
     Note that in problems of this kind you must consider
     overlapping squares.

9.   *Solution*
     If we assume that each pair of teams play once on each of their home fields, we can interpret
     the ordered pairs (A, B) and (B, A) as A playing at B's field and B playing at A's field. The
     number of these ordered pairs gives the number of games played.
     There are 10 choices for the first team of the pair and 9 choices for the second team.
     Thus there are $10\times9=90$ pairs and so the total number of games played is 90.

10. *Solution*
     Let the entry in the lower right square be
     represented by a.
     Then $y\times1\times a=2\times x\times a$
     $$ay=2ax.$$
     Since $a\neq0$, $y=2x$ gives the relation between x
     and y.
     Try some numerical values to verify this.

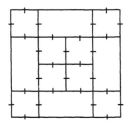

11. *Solution*

We need three consecutive primes, each greater than 65, whose sum is 235.

The average of the primes is $\frac{235}{3} \doteq 78$, and so one, at least, must be greater than 78.

The only prime in the seventies are $71, 73,$ and 79. These sum to 223 and so we need a prime that is larger than 79.

The next prime larger than 79 is 83 and $73 + 79 + 83 = 235$.

Thus the oldest person was 83 in 1995 and this person was born in $1995 - 83 = 1912$.

Are there any other possible answers?

12. *Solution*

Since the sums along each of the four sides are equal, the sum of the numbers on all four sides must be a multiple of four.

Since the sum of the integers from 1 to 9 is 45, the possible sums of the four sides are $44, 40,$ and 36. (Why not 32?)

Hence $1, 5,$ and 9 are the possible numbers that could be placed in the middle circle.

You should check and see if each of these is possible using the given information.

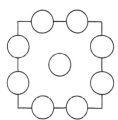

13. *Solution*

There are 101 integers in the set.

There are $10 + 9 = 19$ numbers which contain a 7, namely, $70, 71, ..., 79,$ and $7, 17, 27, ..., 67, 87, 97$.

The probability that at least one of the digits of the integer chosen is a 7 is $\frac{19}{101}$.

14. *Solution*

In 15 hours, the troops can march $15 \times 4 = 60$ km. Thus Bo knows he can only march 60 km before he reaches either the canal or an oasis to replenish his water supply.

Since the distance from A to B is greater than 60 km, the troops must march to the canal.

Let the path taken by the troops be $ADEB$.

Using the Pythagorean Theorem,

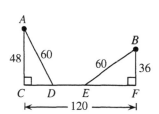

$$CD = \sqrt{60^2 - 48^2}$$
$$= \sqrt{1296}$$
$$= 36.$$

$$\text{and } EF = \sqrt{60^2 - 36^2}$$
$$= \sqrt{2304}$$
$$= 48.$$

Therefore $DE = 120 - (36 + 48) = 36$.

The shortest length for the march is $60 + 36 + 60 = 156$ km and the time required is $156 \div 4 = 39$ hours.

15. *Solution*

In order to make S as large as possible we use the largest x value with the smallest y value.

Thus $S \leq 12 - 6 = 6$.

For the smallest S value, use the smallest x value with the largest y value.

Thus $S \geq 4 - 10 = -6$.

The largest interval for S is $-6 \leq S \leq 6$.

16. *Solution*

Between 200 and 300, the first digit of the number must be 2. This implies that the second digit must be at least 3 and the third digit must be at least 4.

When the second digit is 3, the third can be anything from 4 to 9, inclusive, giving six numbers.

When the second digit is 4, the third can be anything from 5 to 9, inclusive, giving five numbers.

Similarly, when the second digit is 5, 6, 7, or 8 there are 4, 3, 2, or 1 choices, respectively, for the third digit.

Thus there are $6 + 5 + 4 + 3 + 2 + 1 = 21$ ascending integers between 200 and 300.

17. *Solution 1*

$$\frac{1}{a} + \frac{1}{b} = \frac{7}{2} \qquad (1)$$

$$\frac{1}{a} - \frac{1}{b} = -\frac{5}{2} \qquad (2)$$

Add (1) and (2):

$$\frac{2}{a} = 1$$

$$a = 2.$$

Subtract (2) from (1):

$$\frac{2}{b} = 6$$

$$b = \frac{1}{3}.$$

Therefore $a + b = 2 + \frac{1}{3} = \frac{7}{3}$.

Solution 2

The two equations may be rewritten as

$$\frac{a+b}{ab} = \frac{7}{2} \qquad (1)$$

and $\quad \dfrac{b-a}{ab} = -\dfrac{5}{2} \qquad (2)$

Adding (1) and (2) gives

$$\frac{2b}{ab} = 1$$

$$a = 2.$$

Substitute $a = 2$ in the first equation to give

$$\frac{1}{2} + \frac{1}{b} = \frac{7}{2}$$

$$\frac{1}{b} = 3$$

$$b = \frac{1}{3}.$$

Therefore $a + b = 2 + \frac{1}{3} = \frac{7}{3}$.

18. *Solution*

To cut 90% of the lawn using the riding mower requires 90% of 70 minutes or 63 minutes.
To cut 10% of the lawn using the push mower requires 10% of 5 hours or 30 minutes.
Thus it took 93 minutes to cut the lawn.

19. *Solution*

Since P is part of the first column, P cannot be 1
or 2.
Similarly, since P is in the last row, P cannot be 3.
Finally, since P is in the diagonal, P cannot be 5.
Thus $P = 4$.
The entry below Q must be 4, so Q is either 2 or 3.
But Q is part of the third row so Q cannot be 3.
Hence $Q = 2$.

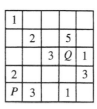

20. *Solution 1*

Of the 45 students, three own neither a bicycle nor a skateboard; therefore $45 - 3 = 42$ own
one or both.
But $27 + 22 = 49$, so the number of students owning both is $49 - 42 = 7$.

Solution 2

If 27 students own a bicycle, then $45 - 27 = 18$ do not own a bicycle.
Since three students own neither a skateboard nor a bicycle, then $18 - 3 = 15$ students own
a skateboard but no bicycle.
Hence there are $22 - 15 = 7$ students who own both a skateboard and a bicycle.

21. *Solution*

Every cube on the outer layer of the block will have at least one painted surface.
If the outer layer of cubes is removed the dimensions of the block will be $8 \times 6 \times 2$ giving a
total of 96 cubes, none of which will have a painted surface.

22. *Solution 1*

If the diameter of the circular opening had been half as large, the area of the circular opening would have been one-quarter as large.

Thus the length of the line of toothpaste would have been four times as long, or $4 \times 10 = 40$ m.

Solution 2

The total volume of toothpaste is $\pi r^2(10)$, where r is the radius of the circular opening. If d m is the length of the new line of toothpaste, then

$$10\pi r^2 = d\pi\left(\frac{1}{2}r\right)^2$$

$$10\pi r^2 = d\pi\frac{r^2}{4}$$

$$40 = d.$$

The new line of toothpaste would be 40 m long.

23. *Solution 1*

If the base of the triangle is increased by 10%, its length is multiplied by 1.1.

To maintain the same area, its height must be multiplied by $\frac{1}{1.1}$.

But $\frac{1}{1.1} = \frac{10}{11} = 1 - \frac{1}{11}$.

Hence the height must be decreased by $\frac{1}{11}$ or $9\frac{1}{11}\%$.

Solution 2

Let the base be b units long and the altitude h units. The area of the triangle is $\frac{1}{2}bh$.

Thus, if x is the percentage decrease of the altitude, we have

$$\frac{1}{2}(1.1b)[(1-x)h] = \frac{1}{2}bh$$

$$1.1(1-x) = 1$$

$$1-x = \frac{1}{1.1}$$

$$x = 1 - \frac{1}{1.1}$$

$$= 1 - \frac{10}{11}$$

$$= \frac{1}{11}$$

$$= 9\frac{1}{11}\%.$$

The altitude must be decreased by $9\frac{1}{11}\%$ to maintain the same area.

24. *Solution*

As gear A rotates for one minute $10 \times 20 = 200$
teeth will pass any selected point, in particular the
points where gear A meshes with gear B, and where
gear B meshes with gear C.

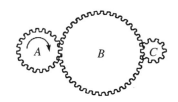

Thus gear C is rotating $\frac{200}{10} = 20$ r.p.m.

Since gear A is rotating clockwise, B will rotate
counter-clockwise and so C is rotating clockwise at
20 r.p.m.

25. *Solution*

We are given that $2W = 3X$ (1)

$$W = Y + Z \quad (2)$$

$$X + Y = Z \quad (3)$$

We must find a relationship between Y and Z.
There are lots of ways to manipulate these
equations.

Here is one that is fairly efficient.

Multiply equation (2) by 2 to give $2W = 2Y + 2Z$ (4)

From (1) and (4) we get $3X = 2Y + 2Z$.

From (3), $3X = 3Z - 3Y$.

Hence $3Z - 3Y = 2Y + 2Z$

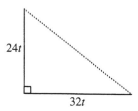

$$Z = 5Y.$$

Five Y's would be required to balance one Z.

26. *Solution*

After t hours the cyclists have travelled $24t$ km and
$32t$ km respectively.

The distance between them is $\sqrt{(24t)^2 + (32t)^2}$.

Solve: $\sqrt{(24t)^2 + (32t)^2} = 130$

$$576t^2 + 1024t^2 = 16\ 900$$

$$1600t^2 = 16\ 900$$

$$t^2 = 10.56$$

$$t \doteq 3.25.$$

They will be 130 km apart $3\frac{1}{4}$ hours after 1:15, that is, at 4:30 p.m.

27. *Solution*
     We have 3 equations:

$$xy = \frac{x}{y} \qquad (1)$$

$$xy = x - y \qquad (2)$$

and $\frac{x}{y} = x - y.$ (3)

Note that since $y \neq 0$, then, from (2) $x \neq 0$.

From (1), $xy^2 = x$

$$y^2 = 1$$

Thus $y = 1$ or $y = -1$.

If $y = 1$, (2) becomes $x = x - 1$ which is impossible and so $y = -1$.

Thus (2) and (3) both become $-x = x + 1$ and so $x = -\frac{1}{2}$.

Thus $x + y = -\frac{3}{2}$.

28. *Solution*
     Consider the length of rope AB.
     Place points C and D so that $AC = CD = DB$.

     If the random cut occurs between A and C, then the
     longer piece will be at least twice as long as the
     shorter piece.

     The probability that the cut occurs between A and C is $\frac{1}{3}$.

     A similar situation occurs if the random cut is between D and B.

     The probability that this happens is again $\frac{1}{3}$.

     If the cut occurs between C and D, the condition is not satisfied.

     Therefore the probability that the longer piece is at least twice as long as the shorter piece

     is $\frac{1}{3} + \frac{1}{3} = \frac{2}{3}$.

29. *Solution*

We must determine the number of cubes required to build each successive structure, and keep a total of all cubes used.

Structure	Number of Layers	Number of Cubes in Structure	Total Number of Cubes Used
1	2	$1^2 + 2^2 = 5$	5
2	3	$5 + 3^2 = 14$	19
3	4	$14 + 4^2 = 30$	49
4	5	$30 + 5^2 = 55$	104
5	6	$55 + 6^2 = 91$	195
6	7	$91 + 7^2 = 140$	335
7	8	$140 + 8^2 = 204$	539
8	9	$204 + 9^2 = 285$	824
9	10	$285 + 10^2 = 385$	

Since structure nine requires 385 cubes, and since $824 + 385 > 1000$, structure nine cannot be built. The first eight structures require a total of 824 cubes, leaving $1000 - 824 = 176$ cubes unused.

We could generalize this problem by noting that structure $n-1$ consists of n layers, and the number of cubes in structure $n-1$ is

$$1^2 + 2^2 + 3^2 + \cdots + n^2 = \frac{n(n+1)(2n+1)}{6}.$$

30. *Solution*

Since the account changes by amounts that are powers of 2 (increasing if the exponent is even and decreasing if it is odd), we must write 114 as the sum and/or difference of powers of 2.

$114 = 256 - 128 - 32 + 16 + 4 - 2$

$= (-1)^8 2^8 + (-1)^7 2^7 + (-1)^5 2^5 + (-1)^4 2^4 + (-1)^2 2^2 + (-1)^1 2^1$

That is, the 8th, 7th, 5th, 4th, 2nd, and first switches must be turned on. Therefore six switches must be turned ON.

31. *Solution*

Let p days represent the time required to wrap one parcel and c days represent the time required to wrap one catalog.

Then $60p + 70c = 1$ (1)

$80p + 40c = 1$ (2)

Thus $60p + 20c = 80p + 40c$

$30c = 20p$ (3)

Substituting into (1): $3(20p) + 70c = 1$

$$3(30c) + 70c = 1$$
$$160c = 1$$
$$c = \frac{1}{160}.$$

Hence the machine wraps 160 catalogues per day.

On Wednesday, Thursday and Friday a total of 480 catalogs were wrapped and together with the 110 wrapped on Monday and Tuesday, a total of 590 catalogs were wrapped that week.

32.   *Solution*

Under the given conditions, neither the 1 nor the 3 can be used in the tens or thousands positions. The 9 must always be used in one of these positions.

If the 9 and the 5 are used in the tens and thousands positions, the five digit numbers satisfying the conditions are   79351, 79153, 35197, 15397.

If the 9 and the 7 are used in the tens and thousands positions the five digit numbers satisfying the conditions are 19573, 19375, 39175, 39571, 59173, 59371, 17593, 17395, 37195, 37591, 57193, 57391.

In total, there are 16 such numbers.

33.   *Solution*

Adding any two elements from the set gives a unique sum between 3 and 89.

Thus the number of integers from 3 to 89 which can be expressed as the sum of two elements from the set is the number of distinct pairs of elements which can be formed from the numbers in A.

There are 9 choices for the first element and 8 for the second for a total of 72.

However this counts each pair twice so there are 36 distinct pairs which can be formed from the numbers in the set.

Thus there are $87 - 36 = 51$ numbers from 3 to 89 which cannot be expressed as the sum of two elements from A.

Chapter 8   Solutions

1. *Solution*
    Let the runner starting from A run at a metres per minute and the one from B at b metres per minute.
    Let the track length be d metres.
    If they meet the first time 600 m from A, this means that the runner from A travels 600 m and the one from B travels $(d - 600)$ m . In travelling these distances, their times must be equal.

    Thus, $\dfrac{600}{a} = \dfrac{d - 600}{b}$.   (1)

    When they meet the second time, the runner coming from A has travelled $(d + 300)$ metres and the one from B has travelled $(2d - 300)$ metres. Again, they have travelled the same length of time.

    It follows that $\dfrac{d + 300}{a} = \dfrac{2d - 300}{b}$.   (2)

    Dividing equation (1) by equation (2) and simplifying we obtain

    $$\frac{600}{d + 300} = \frac{d - 600}{2d - 300}$$
    $$d^2 - 1500d = 0$$
    $$d(d - 1500) = 0.$$

    Therefore $d = 0$ or $d = 1500$ m.
    The track length is 1500 m.

2. *Solution*
    Let a and b be the respective velocities of the faster and slower ship, in metres per second. Consider the problem when the ships are travelling in the same direction and then when they travel in opposite directions.

    (i)   Same Direction
    In 25 seconds the faster ship must travel 300 metres farther than the slower one, with this distance covered at $(a - b)$ metres per second.

    Thus, $\dfrac{300}{a - b} = 25$
    $$a - b = 12.$$

    (ii)   Opposite Direction
    In 10 seconds, the ships travel a total distance of 300 metres. This implies that a distance of 300 m must be covered at $(a + b)$ metres per second.

    Thus, $\dfrac{300}{a + b} = 10$
    $$a + b = 30.$$

    By adding we find, $(a + b) + (a - b) = 42$.
    Therefore $a = 21$.
    The faster ship travels at 21 metres per second.

3.   *Solution*

It would be valuable to see what the assistant earned in the early weeks.

In week one, he earns 1 dollar.

In week two, he earns $1+(1\times 2)$ dollars.

In week three, he earns $1+(1\times 2)+(2\times 2)$ dollars.

In week four, he earns $1+(1\times 2)+(2\times 2)+(3\times 2)$ dollars.

In week five, he earns $1+1\times 2+2\times 2+3\times 2+4\times 2$ dollars.

The pattern now seems definite.

In week fifty-two, he earns $1+1\times 2+2\times 2+3\times 2+4\times 2+5\times 2+\ldots+51\times 2$ dollars.

This sum is $1+2(1+2+3+4+\ldots+51)$

$$=1+2\left(\frac{51\times 52}{2}\right) \qquad (1)$$

$$=1+2652$$

$$=2653.$$

The assistant earns \$2653 in the 52nd week.

Note: If you do not remember the formula used in (1), realize that $1+2+3+\ldots+51$ is the sum of 51 numbers whose average is $\dfrac{1+51}{2}=26$. Thus, the sum is $51\times 26=1326$.

4.   *Solution*

The terms of the series begin at 5.5 and never exceed $5.\overline{55}=5\tfrac{5}{9}$.

(a)   Each term beyond the first term is greater than 5.5.

Thus, $S_{100}=5.5+5.55+5.555+\cdots+\underbrace{5.55\cdots 5}_{100\ 5s}$

$$>5.5+5.5+5.5+\qquad\cdots+5.5$$
$$=100\times 5.5$$
$$=550$$

Since each term in S_n is less than 5.6, $S_{100}<100\times 5.6$
$$=560.$$

Hence $550<S_{100}<560$.

(b)   Since each term of the series is less than $5\tfrac{5}{9}$,

$$S_{100}=5.5+5.55+5.555+\cdots+5.55\cdots 5$$
$$<100\times 5\tfrac{5}{9}=555\tfrac{5}{9}.$$

Therefore $S_{100}<556$.

5.   *Solution*

The sequence is: $p, q, p+q, p+2q, 2p+3q, 3p+5q, 5p+8q, 8p+13q, 13p+21q,$ $21p+34q$.

The seventh term is $t_7 = 5p+8q = 181$.   (1)

The sum of the ten terms is $S_{10} = 55p+88q$

$$= 11(5p+8q)$$
$$= 11(181)$$
$$= 1991.$$

The sum of the sequence is 1991 for all sequences where (p,q) satisfies equation (1). The two sequences that satisfy the given conditions are found by solving the diophantine equation (1).

From (1), $p = \dfrac{181-8q}{5}$.

In order that p be a positive integer, $8q$ must be an integer with a units digit of 6. The values of q that satisfy this condition are: 2, 7, 12, 17, 22.

Since $p < q$, the two sequences are determined by $(p,q)=(1,22)$ and $(p,q)=(9,17)$.

6.   *Solution*

In order to find the required sum, we will write in some entries and look for a pattern. In such circumstances, it is best to leave numbers in their factored form.

Rows $\longrightarrow$

		1	2	3	4	5	6	7	8	9	10
	1	1×2	1×5	•	•	•				1×26	1×29
	2	3×2	3×5	•	•	•				3×26	3×29
	3	5×2	5×5	•	•	•					
Columns	4	•	•								
	5	•	•								
	6	•	•								
	7										
	8										
	9										
	10	19×2								19×26	19×29

The sum of column one is $2\times1+2\times3+2\times5+\ldots+2\times19$

$$= 2(1+3+5+\ldots+19).$$

The sum of column two is $5\times1+5\times3+5\times5+\ldots+5\times19$

$$= 5(1+3+5+\ldots+19).$$

From this we can see that the overall sum is

$2y + 5y + 8y + \ldots + 29y = y(2 + 5 + 8 + \ldots + 29)$, where $y = 1 + 3 + \ldots + 19$.

We can find y by pairing terms of the series front to back.

Therefore $y = (1 + 19) + (3 + 17) + (5 + 15) + (7 + 13) + (9 + 11)$

$$= 5(20)$$

$$= 100.$$

Similarly we find $2 + 5 + 8 + \ldots + 29 = 155$.

The sum of all the elements in the array is $155(100)$ or $15\,500$.

7. *Solution*

This problem can best be solved with the use of a telescoping series. (The series is called 'telescoping' because it collapses in exactly the same way as a telescope.) If we substitute $n = 2, 3, 4, \ldots, 50$ into the given expression we have

$$t_2 - t_1 = 7$$
$$t_3 - t_2 = 9$$
$$t_4 - t_3 = 11$$
$$\vdots$$
$$t_{48} - t_{47} = 99$$
$$t_{49} - t_{48} = 101$$
$$t_{50} - t_{49} = 103.$$

Now, by adding on the left side we find that

$$\left(t_2 - t_1\right) + \left(t_3 - t_2\right) + \left(t_4 - t_3\right) + \ldots + \left(t_{49} - t_{48}\right) + \left(t_{50} - t_{49}\right) = t_{50} - t_1.$$

Thus, $t_{50} - t_1 = 7 + 9 + 11 + \ldots + 99 + 101 + 103$.

Since $t_1 = 5$, $t_{50} = 5 + 7 + 9 + \ldots + 99 + 101 + 103$

$$= \underbrace{(5 + 103) + (7 + 101) + (9 + 99) + \ldots}_{25 \text{ pairs of } 108}$$

$$= 2700.$$

The value of t_{50} is 2700.

8. *Solution 1*

In solving this problem, we must first recognize that an odd integer is always of the form $2n + 1$.

The best way of representing the 28 consecutive integers is: $2n - 27, 2n - 25, \ldots, 2n - 3, 2n - 1, 2n + 1, \ldots, 2n + 25, 2n - 27$.

This may seem a little contrived but when we find their sum it works out to be a simple expression because every integer has an element with which it can be paired.

Pairing and summing we have

$$\left[(2n - 27) + (2n + 27)\right] + \left[(2n - 25) + (2n + 25)\right] + \ldots + \left[(2n - 1) + (2n + 1)\right]$$

$$= 14(4n)$$

$$= 56n.$$

Now, $56n = p^3$.

Factoring, $2^3 \cdot 7n = p^3$.

Since we want the right side to be a perfect cube, $n = 7^2 = 49$.

If $n = 49$, the set of 28 consecutive odd integers is 71, 73, 75, ..., 123, 125.

The smallest integer in this set is 71.

Solution 2

Let the 28 consecutive, odd integers be $p,\ p+2,\ p+4,\ p+6, ...,\ p+54$.

The sum of these 28 odd integers is $p+(p+2)+(p+4)+(p+6)+...+(p+54)$

$$= 28p + (2 + 4 + 6 + ... + 54)$$
$$= 28p + 2(1 + 2 + 3 + ... + 27)$$
$$= 28p + 2\left(\frac{27 \times 28}{2}\right)$$
$$= 28p + 27 \times 28$$
$$= 28(p + 27)$$
$$= \left(2^2\right)(7)(p + 27).$$

Since the sum must be a perfect cube, the least possible value of p is the one for which $p + 27 = (2)\left(7^2\right)$.

Therefore $p + 27 = 98$ and $p = 71$.

It follows that the set of 28 consecutive, odd integers is 71, 73, 75, ..., 123, 125.

The smallest integer in this set is 71.

9.   *Solution*

If we wish to find the speed of the satellite, we need to find the distance it travels over a 24 hour period. In order to do this, it is necessary to calculate the circumference of its circular orbit.

We start by calculating the radius of the earth.

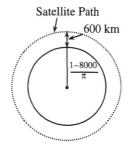

Satellite Path

Using $C = 2\pi r$, we find $r = \dfrac{36\,000}{2\pi} = \dfrac{18\,000}{\pi}$.

Since the circular path of the satellite has a radius 600 km greater than that of the earth, its radius will be $\dfrac{18\,000}{\pi} + 600$.

Its circumference will then be

$$2\pi\left(\frac{18\,000}{\pi} + 600\right) = 2\pi\left(\frac{18\,000}{\pi}\right) + 2\pi(600)$$
$$= 36\,000 + 1200\pi.$$

If the satellite travels a distance of $36\,000 + 1200\pi$ km in 24 hours then its average speed, in km/h, will be

$$\frac{36000 + 1200\pi}{24} = 1500 + 50\pi$$

$$\doteq 1657 \text{ km/h.}$$

10. *Solution*

As was illustrated in the introductory problems, usually the best strategy in dealing with problems involving divisors is to factor the numbers in question.

Since $1996 = 2^2 \times 499$, we have:

$$1996^{1996} = \left(2^2 \times 499\right)^{1996}$$

$$= 2^{3992} \times 499^{1996}.$$

The divisors of 2^{3992} and 499^{1996} that are perfect squares are listed in columns A and B. (If a number is a perfect square, it must have an even exponent.)

A	B
1	1
2^2	499^2
2^4	499^4
$\vdots$	$\vdots$
2^{3992}	499^{1996}

The total number of divisors in column A is 1997, and in column B is 999.

For each of the 1997 divisors in column A, there are 999 divisors in column B, thus making a total of $1997 \times 999 = 1\,995\,003$ divisors that are perfect squares.

11. *Solution*

Since $f(x) = px + q$, then $f(f(x)) = p(px + q) + q$

$$= p^2 x + pq + q.$$

Similarly $f(f(f(x))) = p^2(px + q) + pq + q$

$$= p^3 x + p^2 q + pq + q$$

$$= 8x + 21.$$

By comparison, $p^3 = 8$ and $p^2 q + pq + q = 21$.

Therefore $p = 2$ and $q = 3$ and so $p + q = 5$.

12. *Solution*

The capacity of each section in the horizontal positions is $4 \times 4 \times 4 = 64$ cm^3.

When the tray is tipped, P will lose the volume of a triangular prism whose cross-sectional area is $\triangle ABC$ and whose length is 4 cm.

Since ABC is a $60° - 30° - 90°$ triangle with $AC = 4$ cm, then $AB = \dfrac{4}{\sqrt{3}}$ cm.

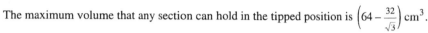

Thus, the volume of the prism is

$$\frac{1}{2}\left(\frac{4}{\sqrt{3}}\right)(4)(4) = \frac{32}{\sqrt{3}} \text{ cm}^3.$$

The maximum volume that any section can hold in the tipped position is $\left(64 - \dfrac{32}{\sqrt{3}}\right)$ cm^3.

The volume of water in R equals the original volume in Q, plus the amount that spills from P, minus the capacity of Q in the tipped position.

Thus the volume of R is $(2 \times 4 \times 4) + \left(\dfrac{32}{\sqrt{3}}\right) - \left(64 - \dfrac{32}{\sqrt{3}}\right) = \left(64 - \dfrac{32}{\sqrt{3}}\right)$ cm^3.

13. *Solution 1*

To find the tiled area we must find the area of one of the octagons.

Subdivide the octagon as shown.

Each corner triangle is an isosceles right-angled triangle.

Using the Pythagorean Theorem, $x^2 + x^2 = 1$, so

$x = \dfrac{1}{\sqrt{2}}$.

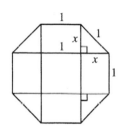

The area of each corner triangle is $\dfrac{1}{2}\left(\dfrac{1}{\sqrt{2}}\right)^2 = \dfrac{1}{4}$ and the area of each of the four

rectangles is $1\left(\dfrac{1}{\sqrt{2}}\right) = \dfrac{1}{\sqrt{2}}$.

The area of the octagon is $1 + 4\left(\dfrac{1}{\sqrt{2}}\right) + 4\left(\dfrac{1}{4}\right) = 2 + 2\sqrt{2}$.

The total tiled area is $4\left(2 + 2\sqrt{2}\right) + 1 = 9 + 8\sqrt{2}$ or approximately 20.3.

Solution 2
Enclose the complete pattern in a square, as shown.
Using the same method as Solution 1, we find that
in each of the small triangles, the sides about the

right angle are $\frac{1}{\sqrt{2}}$, so the area is $\frac{1}{4}$.

Thus the large square has sides of length

$$2+4\left(\frac{1}{\sqrt{2}}\right)=2+2\sqrt{2}.$$

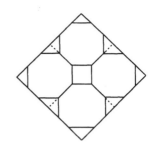

The area of the large square is

$$\left(2+2\sqrt{2}\right)^2 = 12+8\sqrt{2}.$$

Therefore the tiled area is $12+8\sqrt{2}-12\left(\frac{1}{4}\right)=9+8\sqrt{2}$, or approximately 20.3.

14.   *Solution*
Let the original number of employees in the company be e where e is a perfect square.

From the first two statements we have $e+100=k^2+1$.   (1)

From the third statement we increase the number of employees by 100 to obtain

$$(e+100)+100=t^2$$

or $e+200=t^2$.   (2)

Subtracting equations (1) and (2) and then rearranging, we obtain

$$t^2-k^2=101.$$

By factoring the left side and recognizing that 101 is prime we find $(t-k)(t+k)=1\times101$.

Since $t-k$ is smaller than $t+k$ we write

$$t-k=1$$

and $t+k=101$.

By adding, $t=51$ and $k=50$.

By substitution in (2) we find the original number of employees in the company to be 2401.

15.   *Solution*
First consider the face containing PQ and label
PQ as $2x$. If we extend PQ in both directions so
that the extended lines meet the cube edges we can

then label these measures as $\left(\dfrac{10-2x}{2}\right)$ or $5-x$.

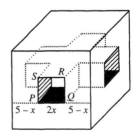

It is tempting to think that the cut out shape is made
up of 5 identical cubes but it is not. Four of the
shapes are rectangular solids with dimensions $2x$,
$2x$ and $5-x$ with the centre solid (a cube) having
dimensions $2x$, $2x$ and $2x$.

Since the volume of the part that is removed is one-
half the volume of the original cube we have

$$4[(2x)(2x)(5-x)]+(2x)(2x)(2x)=500.$$

Rearranging and simplifying we have

$$80x^2-16x^3+8x^3=500$$

or $\quad 2x^3-20x^2+125=0$.

If we try different values of x and put them in a table we obtain

x	$2x^3 - 20x^2 + 125$
1	107
2	61
3	−1
2.99	−.340
2.98	.319

From these calculations we can see that $PQ \doteq 2(2.985) \doteq 6.0$ (to the nearest tenth).

16. *Solution*

After rotating the rectangle, construct $\triangle AEB'$ and
label the diagram as shown.
We know that $\angle EAB'$ equals 45° making $\triangle AEB'$
isosceles and right angled.
It is given that $AB' = 4$, thus making

$AE = EB' = 2\sqrt{2}$.

As a result, the height of $\triangle PQB'$ is $2\sqrt{2}-1$.
Using similar reasoning as before, $\triangle PRB'$ is
isosceles and right-angled making

$PR = RQ = \sqrt{2}-1$.

Therefore the area of $\triangle PQB'$ is

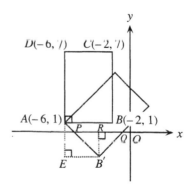

$$\tfrac{1}{2}(2\sqrt{2}-1)[(2)(2\sqrt{2}-1)]=(2\sqrt{2}-1)(2\sqrt{2}-1)$$
$$=9-4\sqrt{2}.$$

The area of the portion of the rectangle that is
above the x-axis is $24-(9-4\sqrt{2})=15+4\sqrt{2}$

$$\doteq 20.7 \text{ square units.}$$

17. *Solution 1*

Let the coordinates of A and B be $(0, a)$ and $(0, b)$, respectively.

Since the area of $\triangle AOC$ is 108, we have

$$\frac{(OA)(OC)}{2} = 54$$

or $\quad \dfrac{(a)(OC)}{2} = 54.$

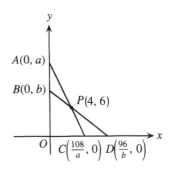

Thus, $OC = \dfrac{108}{a}.$

Therefore the coordinates of C are $\left(\dfrac{108}{a}, 0\right)$.

In the same way, D has $\left(\dfrac{96}{b}, 0\right)$ as its coordinates.

In order to find the value of a, we use the fact that slope PA = slope CP.

$$\frac{a-6}{-4} = \frac{6}{4 - \dfrac{108}{a}}$$

$$\frac{a-6}{-4} = \frac{6a}{4a - 108}.$$

Multiplying out and simplifying, we find

$$a^2 - 27a + 162 = 0$$

$$(a-18)(a-9) = 0.$$

Therefore $a = 18$ or $a = 9$.

Similarly, to find b, we use the fact that slope PB = slope DP.

$$\frac{b-6}{-4} = \frac{6}{4 - \dfrac{96}{b}}$$

$$\frac{b-6}{-4} = \frac{6b}{4b - 96}.$$

Simplifying, we get $b^2 - 24b + 144 = 0$

$$(b-12)^2 = 0.$$

Thus $b = 12$.

Since $a > b$, $a = 18$ and $b = 12$.

The coordinates of C are $(6, 0)$ and the coordinates of D are $(8, 0)$.

The area of $\triangle PCD = \dfrac{1}{2}(2)(6) = 6.$

Solution 2

The family of lines through P has equation

$y - 6 = m(x - 4)$.

The y-intercept is $-4m + 6$ and the x-intercept is

$\dfrac{4m - 6}{m}$.

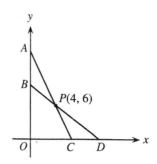

Since the area of $\triangle AOC$ is 54, then

$$\frac{1}{2}(-4m + 6)\left(\frac{4m - 6}{m}\right) = 54$$

$$-16m^2 + 48m - 36 = 108m$$

$$4m^2 + 15m + 9 = 0$$

$$(4m + 3)(m + 3) = 0$$

$$m = -\frac{3}{4} \quad \text{or} \quad m = -3.$$

If $m = -\dfrac{3}{4}$, the x-intercept is 12 and the coordinates of C are $(12, 0)$.

If $m = 3$, the x-intercept is 6 and the coordinates of C are $(6, 0)$.

Since the area of $\triangle BOD$ is 48, then

$$\frac{1}{2}(-4m + 6)\left(\frac{4m - 6}{m}\right) = 48$$

$$-16m^2 + 48m - 36 = 96m$$

$$4m^2 + 12m + 9 = 0$$

$$(2m + 3)^2 = 0$$

$$m = -\frac{3}{2}.$$

If $m = -\dfrac{3}{2}$, the x-intercept is 8 and the coordinates of D are $(8, 0)$.

Since $AO > BO$, the coordinates of C must be $(6, 0)$.

Thus $CD = 8 - 6 = 2$ and the area of $\triangle PCD$ is $\dfrac{1}{2}(2)(6) = 6$.

18. *Solution*

Label the diagram as shown and join A to R and C to T.

Using the same reasoning as in introductory problem 3, we find the following:

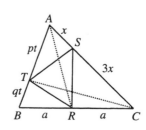

$w = \triangle CRS = \dfrac{3}{4}\triangle ARC = \dfrac{3}{4}\left(\dfrac{1}{2}y\right) = \dfrac{3}{8}y$, where y is the

area of $\triangle ABC$.

$$x = \Delta RBT = \frac{q}{p+q} \Delta ABR = \frac{q}{p+q}\left(\frac{1}{2}y\right) = \frac{q}{2(p+q)}y$$

$$z = \Delta ATS = \frac{1}{4}\Delta ATC = \frac{1}{4}\left(\frac{p}{p+q}y\right) = \frac{p}{4(p+q)}y$$

Since $x^2 = wz$, we have

$$\frac{q^2 y^2}{4(p+q)^2} = \left(\frac{3}{8}y\right)\left(\frac{py}{4(p+q)}\right)$$

$$\frac{q^2}{(p+q)^2} = \frac{3p}{8(p+q)}$$

$$3p^2 + 3pq - 8q^2 = 0.$$

Dividing by q^2, we get $\dfrac{3p^2}{q^2} + 3\dfrac{p}{q} - 8 = 0$

$$3\left(\frac{p}{q}\right)^2 + 3\left(\frac{p}{q}\right) - 8 = 0.$$

Therefore $\dfrac{p}{q} = \dfrac{-3 \pm \sqrt{105}}{6}.$

Since $\dfrac{p}{q} > 0$, the required ratio is $\dfrac{-3+\sqrt{105}}{6}$, that is, $p:q = -3+\sqrt{105}:6$.

19. *Solution*

Since we are given values for p^3 and q^3 and want the value of $p+q$, the factorization for the sum of cubes is useful.

Using this factorization we find $p^3 + q^3 = (p+q)(p^2 - pq + q^2)$

$$= (p+q)\left[(p+q)^2 - 3pq\right].$$

But $p^3 + q^3 = \left(5+\sqrt{2}i\right) + \left(5-\sqrt{2}i\right) = 10.$

Therefore $10 = (p+q)\left[(p+q)^2 - 3pq\right].$

We can now find pq because we know $p^3 q^3 = \left(5+\sqrt{2}i\right)\left(5-\sqrt{2}i\right) = 25+2 = 27.$

Thus $pq = 3.$

If we substitute $pq = 3$ and let $p+q$ be represented by x, we find $10 = x\left(x^2 - 9\right).$

Rewriting gives $0 = x^3 - 9x - 10.$

Using the factor theorem, we find $f(-2) = (-2)^3 - 9(-2) - 10 = 0.$

From this, $x+2$ is a factor of $x^3 - 9x - 10.$

To find the other factors we divide:

$$x + 2 \overline{)\begin{array}{l} x^2 - 2x - 5 \\ x^3 + 0x^2 - 9x - 10 \end{array}}$$

$$\underline{x^3 + 2x^2}$$

$$-2x^2 - 9x$$

$$\underline{-2x^2 - 4x}$$

$$-5x - 10$$

$$\underline{-5x - 10}$$

$$0$$

We can see that $p + q = -2$ and, because the roots of $x^2 - 2x - 5 = 0$ are irrational, then there is only one integral value of $p + q$, namely -2.

20. *Solution 1*

This equation is best solved if we first write it as $a^{\frac{1}{3}} - b^{\frac{1}{3}} = 3$, where $a = x + 9$ and $b - x - 9$.

We can simplify this by cubing both sides, $\left(a^{\frac{1}{3}} - b^{\frac{1}{3}} \right)^3 = 3$.

Therefore $a - 3a^{\frac{2}{3}}b^{\frac{1}{3}} + 3a^{\frac{1}{3}}b^{\frac{2}{3}} - b = 27$.

Rearranging and factoring we obtain $a - b - 3a^{\frac{1}{3}}b^{\frac{1}{3}}\left(a^{\frac{1}{3}} - b^{\frac{1}{3}} \right) = 27$.

Note: $a - b = (x + 9) - (x - 9) = 18$ and $a^{\frac{1}{3}} - b^{\frac{1}{3}} = 3$.

Now we substitute to obtain $18 - 3a^{\frac{1}{3}}b^{\frac{1}{3}}(3) = 27$.

Simplifying we have $a^{\frac{1}{3}}b^{\frac{1}{3}} = -1$ or $[(x + 9)(x - 9)]^{\frac{1}{3}} = -1$, where $a = x + 9$ and $b = x - 9$.

Cubing again gives $\left[[(x + 9)(x + 9)]^{\frac{1}{3}} \right]^3 = (-1)^3$

$$(x + 9)(x - 9) = -1$$

$$x^2 - 81 = -1$$

$$x^2 = 80.$$

The value of x^2 is 80.

Solution 2

Rewrite $\sqrt[3]{x+9}-\sqrt[3]{x-9}=3$ as $\sqrt[3]{x+9}=3+\sqrt[3]{x-9}$.

Cubing both sides gives $x+9=27+27\sqrt[3]{x-9}+9\sqrt[3]{(x-9)^2}+x-9$.

$$27\sqrt[3]{x-9}+9\sqrt[3]{(x-9)^2}=-9$$
$$3\sqrt[3]{x-9}+\sqrt[3]{(x-9)^2}=-1$$
$$\sqrt[3]{x-9}\left[3+\sqrt[3]{x-9}\right]=-1.$$

But $3+\sqrt[3]{x-9}=\sqrt[3]{x+9}$, so $\sqrt[3]{x-9}\sqrt[3]{x+9}=-1$.

Cubing both sides gives $(x-9)(x+9)=-1$

$$x^2-81=-1.$$

As before, we get $x^2=80$.

Note that we can approximate the value of x^2 by choosing appropriate values of x and using a calculator.

If $x=9$, $\sqrt[3]{x+9}-\sqrt[3]{x-9}\approx2.62$.

If $x=8.8$, $\sqrt[3]{x+9}-\sqrt[3]{x-9}\approx3.2$.

Thus, if $8.8<x<9$, then $77<x^2<81$.

21. *Solution*

If we imagine that the cylindrical shape is opened up to form a rectangle and we put the given information on the diagram and label appropriately we would have the following:

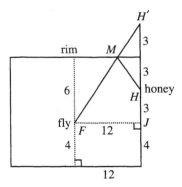

In order to reach the honey, the fly would walk to the rim and then over to reach the honey on the other side.

Since we are requiring that the fly walks the shortest distance, think of the rim as a mirror and reflect H in the mirror to find its image. The distance that is required is FH'.

We know that length FJ is 12 units, or half the circumference, and that JH' is 9 units.

Therefore $(FH')^2=9^2+12^2=225$, so $FH'=15$.

The shortest distance is $FH'=FM+MH=15\text{ cm}$.

22. *Solution*

By symmetry, T is at the midpoint of BC.
By properties of the circle, the right bisector of CB
will pass through T, the midpoint of BC, and be
parallel to AC.
By symmetry, OT extended will meet the circle at R.
Since C is on the semicircle, angle C equals $90°$,
thus making $\triangle ACB$ isosceles and right-angled.

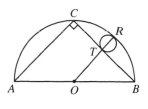

Therefore, $AC = BC = \sqrt{2}$.

Using the fact that $\triangle BTO$ is isosceles and right-angled, $OT = \dfrac{1}{2}AC = \dfrac{\sqrt{2}}{2}$.

We can now calculate TR since $OR = OT + TR$, $OR = 1$ and $OT = \dfrac{\sqrt{2}}{2}$.

Thus, $TR = 1 - \dfrac{\sqrt{2}}{2} = \dfrac{2-\sqrt{2}}{2}$ and the required radius is $\dfrac{1}{2}\left(\dfrac{2-\sqrt{2}}{2}\right) = \dfrac{2-\sqrt{2}}{4} \doteq 0.15.$

23. *Solution*

Since the point C lies on the semicircle, angle C
equals $90°$.
Because $\triangle ABC$ is isosceles with $AB = 2$, then
$AC = BC = \sqrt{2}$.
Using properties of circles, we know that the right
bisector of any chord will pass through the centre O.
Construct the right bisector of BC and label its
midpoint as Q.
By symmetry, if we extend the line segment OQ it
will meet the midpoint of DE at P.
In $\triangle OQB$, which is also isosceles and right angled,
we have $OB = 1$ so $OQ = \dfrac{1}{\sqrt{2}}$.

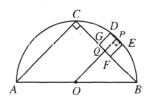

For convenience, let the side of square $GDEF$ be
$2x$ so $PQ = 2x$ and $PE = x$.
Consider $\triangle OPE$ with the sides labelled as shown.
Note that $OE = 1$ because it is the radius of the
circle.

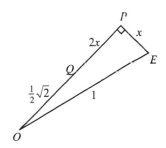

Therefore $\left(2x + \dfrac{1}{2}\sqrt{2}\right)^2 + x^2 = 1$

$$10x^2 + 4\sqrt{2}x - 1 = 0.$$

Using the quadratic formula, we obtain $x = \dfrac{\sqrt{2}}{10}$.

The area of the square is $4x^2 = 4\left(\dfrac{\sqrt{2}}{10}\right)^2$

$$= \dfrac{2}{25}.$$